# REPORT ON

## THE

# ATOM

# REPORT ON THE ATOM

*What You Should Know
About the Atomic Energy Program
of the United States*

B Y

## GORDON DEAN

*Former Chairman, U.S. Atomic Energy Commission
1950–1953*

1953

ALFRED A KNOPF  NEW YORK

L. C. catalog card number: 53–6849

THIS IS A BORZOI BOOK,
PUBLISHED BY ALFRED A. KNOPF, INC.

FIRST EDITION

# PREFACE

## *The Why of This Book*

I CANNOT RECALL just when the idea of writing a book on atomic energy first occurred to me. I think it developed in nebulous form in the first few weeks after my appointment to the Atomic Energy Commission in 1949, when I was trying to educate myself about the American atomic energy program as fast as possible. I soon discovered that this was not easy. While there was much information available, most of it was either too technical or altogether too popular to be of much real value to the average adult citizen. At one end of the scale were literally tons of books and papers prepared for the chemist, the physicist, and the engineer. At the other were a good many volumes and pamphlets, even comic books, designed to explain the atom and the fission process to the layman. Unfortunately, outside of the government's official reports, there was very little in between these two extremes; very little, that is, that attempted to describe the atomic energy program itself or to convey a real feeling for the many great problems which face the nation in the atomic energy field— problems with which I, as a Commissioner, would have to deal. It was about at this point, I think, that I knew I must try my hand at a book which would help fill this void.

This is not a technical book. If it were, I would be the last to attempt to write it. Neither is it a book of personal reminiscences, although it might be more entertaining, albeit less instructive, if it were. Neither is this a posterity letter designed to demonstrate how perfect the atomic energy program was during the days when I had a considerable measure of responsibility for it. Any person in public service who has the rather undramatic job of keeping his nose to the grindstone of administrative duty finds it very hard to appreciate a contemporary who has the time or the inclination to engage in the bureaucratic pastime of "building a record."

Unfortunately, this is also not a book dealing with the people of the atomic energy program who deserve the medals—the people who make the program tick, the devoted backstage heroes on the staffs of the Atomic Energy Commission and its field offices and in the industrial concerns that carry so much of the load.

This book, instead, is an attempt to describe in straightforward and simple terms the major segments of the atomic energy program of the United States, which must be understood by government officials, leaders in industry, and persons in all walks of life if we are to survive and handle ourselves wisely in the atomic age.

About all most people know of the atomic energy program today is that it is big, costly, and complicated, and that it is devoted primarily to bomb-making and may eventually be devoted to more peaceful objectives. I fully appreciate that there are people who do not want to understand any more than this. Some have assumed that secrecy forecloses such understanding. Others assume that atomic energy is so technically complicated that the effort spent in trying to understand it would bear little result. There are still others who, consciously or subconsciously, look upon the atom as something so sinful or frightening that they try to put it out of their minds. None of these reasons supplies a legitimate rationale for continued ignorance in a world where continued ignorance may well be the most sinful and frightening thing of all.

What appears in the following pages is a report on the atom as I know it. That particular atom is made up of many more parts than electrons, protons, and neutrons. Buzzing around, and very close to the nucleus of the atom I know are budgets, appropriations, Congressional hearings, labor disputes, materials shortages, prima donnas, earnest and patriotic people, irresponsible people, and all grades in between: spies, martyrs, civilians, soldiers, heroes, and heretics. It would take many volumes to tell the whole story, but I believe that in this one volume I have touched on the major segments. I hope I have always been factual, except in those portions where I have indicated a drift to opinion. Above all, I hope that this work will shed a little light—if ever so small—on a very dark area, and perhaps also encourage the lighting of other lamps for the unknown paths ahead.

I am indebted to many people for the knowledge I have gained and attempted to report here. I am particularly indebted to Mr. Oliver Townsend, my personal assistant for the past two years, for his frank and unfailing criticism, the highly perceptive quality of his mind, and the sharpness of his editorial pen.

GORDON DEAN
*Las Vegas, Nevada*

# CONTENTS

# CHAPTER 1

## The American Approach to the Atom

LIKE almost everyone else, I first heard of the American atomic energy program on August 6, 1945, when President Truman announced to the people of the United States and of the world:

"Sixteen hours ago an American airplane dropped one bomb on Hiroshima, an important Japanese Army base. That bomb had more power than 20,000 tons of TNT. . . . It is an atomic bomb. . . . The force from which the sun draws its power has been loosed against those who brought war to the Far East."

When this historic announcement was flashed across the news wires of the world, I was in London. I was there as an assistant to Justice Robert H. Jackson, who had been designated to serve as chief prosecutor of the major Nazi war criminals at the forthcoming Nuremberg trials. We were in London to develop with our Allies, the British, the French, and the Russians, a charter setting forth the principles and procedures under which the perpetrators of World War II were to be brought to the bar of justice. The charter had just been agreed upon after eight long weeks of negotiation, and we regarded the date of its signing, August 5, as a significant one, for it branded as criminals not only those who had launched World War II, but also those who would launch all future wars.

Those midsummer days of 1945, when the war against Germany had been won and the final assault against Japan was being mobilized, were fateful ones on many counts, and they held many significant dates. In the two weeks leading up to August 6 and Hiroshima the world had seen the conclusion of the Potsdam Conference, the issuance of the Allied ultimatum against Japan, the approval of the United Nations Charter by the United States Senate, and the signing of the agreement establishing the principles under which the Nuremberg defendants were to be tried. Those were days of destiny and decision, when men wrestled heroically with the fundamental questions of peace and morality while they mobilized their strength and resources for the final push against those who had defied and violated every decent human instinct.

It was into this setting that the atomic bomb burst. Its brilliant light illuminated in stark outline the hopes and fears of mankind for the future, and its towering radioactive cloud hung like a huge question mark over the efforts of those who were striving to establish a permanent code of international morality and a system under which a lasting peace could be built. I well remember the profound impression the news from Hiroshima made upon those of us who were in London.

After the President's initial announcement, news of the atomic bomb and the program that had produced it poured in from Washington, from Hiroshima, from Oak Ridge, from Hanford, from Los Alamos, and then, on August 9, from Nagasaki, the second target city. On August 10, four days after the first atomic bomb had been used in war and 1,342 days after Pearl Harbor, the Japanese formally offered to surrender; and mankind was left to speculate upon the advantages and hazards of existing on a planet that also contained the powerful but unruly atomic genie released at Hiroshima.

During the period immediately following Hiroshima and

Nagasaki, there appeared in the press of the world many moving expressions of fact and fallacy about atomic energy that persist even today. With the information that became available, there also began to be circulated the misinformation that has ever since plagued those who would try to educate the peoples of the world about the atom and its implications.

In the press of the day, for example, one may find reports of how both the Hiroshima and Nagasaki bombs were dropped by parachute. Actually, neither was. One may find also a report on how the Hiroshima bomb caused more damage "because it was exploded in the air." Actually, both bombs were air bursts. There were also learned treatises on how the cities of Hiroshima and Nagasaki would be unfit for human habitation for many years to come because of the radioactivity left behind by the atomic explosions. As we now know, both cities were reoccupied almost immediately without ill effect to those returning. One of the more tragic fallacies was the widely circulated belief that the Japanese were "after the bomb too" because the American occupation forces found a cyclotron in a Japanese university laboratory. In an excess of poorly informed zeal the occupation troops destroyed this valuable research instrument under the impression that it was useful in the development and manufacture of bombs. It of course was not useful for this purpose, but the Japanese scientists nevertheless had to wait seven years before they were in a position to obtain a replacement from an American manufacturer. The Atomic Energy Commission was glad to approve the export of this replacement last year.

Among the facts reported in the British papers of the time were many having to do with the valuable contribution made by British scientists to the American bomb program, first as pioneering research workers in their own laboratories and later as members of the British scientific mission to the United States. The contributions of people like Sir James Chadwick and Professor Rudolf Peierls were described, and mention was made of the work of the German refugee Otto Frisch, as well as of the French scientists Hans von Halban and Leo Kowarski, who escaped to England after the fall of France with forty gallons of heavy water, then practically the entire world stock of this valuable material. Among those to whom a good deal of credit was given for developing the data upon which the calculations of the so-called "critical size" of the bomb were based was one Klaus Fuchs of Birmingham University and the British mission to Los Alamos, who now languishes in a British jail after achieving world-wide notoriety as the "master traitor" of World War II.

The newspapers of the day recorded also all the fears and frustrations and hopes that still motivate the peoples of the earth in their dealings with atomic energy. In fact, as one looks back, it is surprising how little has been added in the ensuing years in the way of new ideas concerning the implications of this new force. As I was in London at the time, most of the initial reactions to the news of the bomb that I heard and read were those of Britons. But they were not just British reactions; they were human reactions, and they were the same all over the world. Thus, in London, in the days immediately following Hiroshima, we were able to read such comments as the following:

"It is indeed on the creative side that this new source of energy presents the most hopeful and fascinating possibilities," said a British government official in the *London Chronicle*. "It may not be rash to predict that, sooner or later, [atomic energy] will establish itself economically as well as scientifically and command the field." This same official went on to express the prophetic opinion that "for the moment, the United States, in terms of power politics, can dominate the world. In comparison Russia is only a

properly pursued, could bring great benefit to the people of the United States and of the world.

3. That the enormous potentiality of the atom for evil as well as good meant that a rather special means had to be developed to control it in such a way that the good could be released and the evil suppressed.

4. That special means of controlling the atom internationally as well as nationally should be developed as matters of great urgency.

5. That, until an effective system of international control could be set up and placed in effect, the United States should continue to hold on to its monopoly in the atomic weapons field.

At no time, so far as I have been able to learn, did anyone in a position of responsibility suggest that "now that we have the bomb exclusively, let us go out and conquer the world." The United States has never thought in such terms, and it did not think in such terms at the conclusion of World War II.

Because of the preliminary thinking that had been given to the question of atomic energy, both formally within the Secretary of War's committee and informally in the halls of government and science, President Truman was able to say in his original announcement about Hiroshima: "I shall recommend that the Congress of the United States consider promptly the establishment of an appropriate commission to control the production and use of atomic power within the United States. I shall give further consideration and make further recommendations to the Congress as to how atomic power can become a powerful and forceful influence towards the maintenance of world peace." Three days later, in an address to the nation, he added: "The atomic bomb is too dangerous to be loose in a lawless world. That is why [we] do not intend to reveal the secret until means have been found to control the bomb so as to protect ourselves and the rest of the world from the danger of total destruction."

Thus it was that the United States began to answer the question of what its approach to the atom was to be. In its broad outline, this approach had three main objectives: (1) to develop and establish an effective system for controlling the atom within the United States; (2) to help develop and establish an effective system for controlling the atom throughout the world; and (3) to hold on to the American monopoly in atomic energy until an international control system had been established, meanwhile using the atom, not for aggression or national aggrandizement, but for the preservation of world peace and the betterment of mankind.

The world, for a time, breathed easier as it watched to see what these noble motives would produce.

The practical problem facing the United States was that of making the wartime bomb program over into a peacetime atomic energy program designed to accommodate the enormous power of the atom for good or evil. The wartime program under the direction of the never-tiring General Groves had been highly successful in achieving the goal for which it had been set up, namely, to develop and put into production an atomic bomb. The United States owes the General a great debt. He succeeded in an almost impossible mission. But the wartime program was hardly suitable as a framework for handling the atom in time of peace. In the first place, it had been started and carried on under the temporary emergency powers of the President which were due to expire after the war had been brought to its formal conclusion. In addition, it was quite obvious that the wartime program was not broadly enough conceived nor deeply enough embedded in the political fabric of the nation to make it an effective instrument for controlling the unleashed atom and realizing its peaceful promise. Something else was needed, but it was clear that this "something else" would have to draw upon the experience gained with the atom in World War II.

A good deal of the information concerning the wartime program became a matter of public record very quickly once the news from Hiroshima had revealed its existence. In the official statements from the White House and the Pentagon, in the feature articles and news dispatches from the newly revealed laboratories and plants, and then, later, in the famous *Smyth Report*, the story began to emerge. It was a dramatic story of prodigious effort, brilliant achievement, devotion to duty, and wholehearted co-operation among many varied groups in government, industry, and science. It was all of these, but perhaps most of all it was the story of a magnificent gamble that paid off. The highlights of this fascinating story, as I see them, are as follows:

January 1939: It was in this month, when the war clouds were gathering over Europe but before actual hostilities had begun, that word arrived in the United States that two German scientists had split the uranium atom. This exciting news circulated quickly through the American scientific community and the German experiment was repeated within a matter of days in a number of American laboratories, as it was in several other laboratories in other parts of the world. Speculative articles began to appear in the press about the enormous amounts of energy that could theoretically be released by a nuclear chain reaction.

August 1939: A group of European refugee scientists, by now living in the United States, early recognized the military possibilities of atomic energy and, fearing German efforts in this direction, organized an attempt to interest the American government in undertaking an atomic research program. After an initial approach to the Navy Department in March 1939, which they did not regard as being very productive, they determined to reach President Roosevelt direct. This was accomplished through the device of a letter of August 2, 1939, signed by Albert Einstein and delivered to the President during a personal conference by the Russian-born New York financier Alexander Sachs. As a result of this approach, the President, at about the same time as World War II began with the German invasion of Poland, appointed a three-man "Uranium Committee" to look into the question of developing an atomic bomb. This committee, on which the Army, the Navy, and the Bureau of Standards were represented, submitted a report to the President in November which described the bomb as "a possibility."

April 1940: By this month the scientists of the free world succeeded in establishing an effective system of voluntary censorship in the field of atomic energy, but not before several earlier attempts to do so had been blocked by Frédéric Joliot of Paris.* Thus the atom, in the month that Norway was invaded, vanished behind a barrier of secrecy from which it has never wholly emerged.

June 1940: It was in this month—the month in which France surrendered to the German blitz—that the United States began a small, integrated atomic research program under the National Defense Research Committee, headed by Dr. Vannevar Bush. From this point until Pearl Harbor the United States spent approximately $300,000 on atomic energy.

December 1941: As a result of optimistic reports from research workers in both the United States and Great Britain, the decision was made about the time of the Pearl Harbor attack to undertake an all-out research and development effort in the atomic energy field with the objective of moving into full-scale production as soon as possible. The entire program was placed under the newly established Office of Scientific Research and Develop-

---

* Apparently, according to the *Smyth Report*, "because of one letter sent in to the *Physical Review* before all Americans had been brought into the agreement."

ment, of which Dr. Bush was placed in charge, with the understanding that later, if and when the construction phase was reached, the whole program would be turned over to the Army. The decisions taken in December meant that the government was embarking on a program for which between four and five million dollars would have to be committed.

June 1942: It was in this month—the month of the Battle of Midway—that President Roosevelt, upon the recommendation of Dr. Bush and with the approval of a policy group composed of Vice President Wallace, Secretary Stimson, General Marshall, and Dr. Conant, made the decision to proceed with the enormous wartime construction program that was ultimately to cost nearly two billion dollars. This was the month when the bets of the "magnificent gamble" were placed.

August 1942: On August 13 the Army established a new district in its Corps of Engineers. It was named the Manhattan Engineer District, and it was given the job of making the magnificent gamble pay off. The following month Major (then Brigadier) General Leslie R. Groves was placed in charge of the new district, and an overseeing Military Policy Committee with Dr. Bush as chairman was set up in the War Department. Immediately the job of selecting sites, contractors, and designs for the projected new plants began under General Groves's very capable direction.

December 1942: Most historians seem to agree that it was actually on December 2, 1942, that the so-called "atomic age" was ushered in. This event took place in secret in a makeshift laboratory in a converted squash court beneath the west stands of the University of Chicago's Stagg Field, where the Italian-born physicist Enrico Fermi and a small staff were working under contract to the Office of Scientific Research and Development on the problem of demonstrating that a self-sustaining nuclear chain reaction could actually be made to work. On the morning of December 2 they did it, and the first atomic pile in the history of the world was operated successfully. Eagerly the code message was relayed to other scientists: "The Italian navigator has landed; the natives are friendly."

May 1943: By this date, all of the research and development work being done in the field of atomic energy had been transferred from the OSRD to the Manhattan Engineer District, which since the previous September had already been in charge of all construction work. From this point forward, therefore, the Manhattan District was in complete charge of the program.

After Hiroshima the Manhattan District's record of achievement became known. It became known, for example, how in a two-and-a-half-year period a secret city, named Oak Ridge, had been hewn out of the East Tennessee wilderness, and how two mammoth bomb-material plants and a large new laboratory, costing in all nearly a billion dollars, had been erected in the 59,000-acre reservation surrounding the town. It also became known how another great plant, costing $350,000,000, had been erected on a 400,000-acre reservation in an isolated part of the Columbia River Valley in the State of Washington, and how another government town, named Richland, had grown up beside it.

It became known how, in the performance of its construction and engineering miracle, the Manhattan District had relied upon the genius of American industry, and how, among many hundreds of others, the following made outstanding contributions: the E. I. duPont de Nemours & Company, the M. W. Kellogg Company, the J. A. Jones Construction Company, the Union Carbide and Carbon Corporation, the Stone and Webster Engineering Corporation, the Tennessee Eastman Company, the Allis-Chalmers Manufacturing Company, the Chrysler Corporation, the General Electric Company, and the Westinghouse Electric Corporation. It also became known how the universities of the country had provided unstinting and invaluable support in scientific matters, with particularly noteworthy contributions having been made by Columbia University, the University of Chicago, the University of California, and Iowa State College.

It became known how the United States had had the valuable assistance of Great Britain and Canada in the bomb development program; how Britain had sent a team of scientists to America for direct participation, and how Canada had a heavy-water plant and a government research laboratory that were co-operating directly with the American program. It became known how the three Allied nations jointly operated a program for the procurement of uranium, and how a Combined Policy Committee, upon which Secretary Stimson, Dr. Bush, and Dr. Conant were the American representatives, had been established in August 1943 to provide over-all policy direction to the co-operative effort of the three nations.

It also became known how a highly secret laboratory had been established on a mesa top at Los Alamos, New Mexico, and how the brilliant physicist J. Robert Oppenheimer from the University of California had been placed in charge with the assignment of designing a workable atomic bomb. It became known how Dr. Oppenheimer assembled a staff of first-rate physicists from the United States and Great Britain around him; how, one day in July 1945, they took the device they had been working on down to the desert near Alamogordo, and how, at dawn of the morning of July 16, they set it off. It also became known how this device performed according to the most optimistic expectations, and how, twenty-one days later, the second one worked just as successfully over Hiroshima in Japan. The gamble had paid off, and a new problem had been deposited on the doorstep of the world.

With the end of the war, the center of interest in the new field of atomic energy shifted from the plants and laboratories of the United States and the target cities of Japan to Washington, D. C., where men were wrestling with the decisions that would determine America's course in the atomic age. From the precedents of the wartime program, and from the hopes and fears of men for the future, they began the arduous job of building a legal structure that would contain the unleashed atom. Meanwhile, the nation's atomic energy program, which had been assembled to develop and produce the bomb, began to mark time while it waited to find out where it was going next. Funds were cut back, the British mission began to pack up and leave for home, and many of the scientists and technicians in the plants and laboratories left the program to return to the universities and industrial concerns from which they had been mobilized. During this period, the once dynamic program was held together, but that is about all one could have said for it, or expected of it.

But if things were quiet on the laboratory front, political activity in Washington was furious. The first development of record occurred four days after the formal Japanese surrender when a freshman Senator from Connecticut, Brien McMahon, introduced a bill for the domestic control of atomic energy. The Congress, which was waiting for the proposals promised by the President in his August 6 announcement on Hiroshima, tabled the bill.

The President's recommendations were forthcoming on October 3 in a message to the Congress on atomic energy. In this message the President said:

"Never in history has society been confronted with a power so full of potential danger and at the same time so full of promise for the future of man and for the peace of the world. I think I express the faith of the American people when I say that we can use the knowledge we have won, not for the devastation of war, but for the future welfare of humanity.

"To accomplish that objective we must proceed along two fronts—the domestic and the international.

"The first and most urgent step is the determination of our domestic policy for the control, use, and development of atomic energy within the United States."

Having thus described the objectives, the President proceeded to urge the Congress to establish "an Atomic Energy Commission with members appointed by the President, with the advice and consent of the Senate." He suggested that the entire program as it then existed be transfered to the new Commission, and that the Commission be authorized "to conduct all necessary research, experimentation, and operations for the further development and use of atomic energy for military, industrial, scientific, or medical purposes." He further proposed that the Congress declare it to be "unlawful to produce or use the substance comprising the source of atomic energy or to import or export them except under conditions prescribed by the Commission."

The President acknowledged that the measures he had suggested were drastic and far-reaching, but pointed out that "the discovery with which we are dealing involves forces of nature too dangerous to fit into any of our usual concepts."

Relative to the world situation, he said: "The hope of civilization lies in international arrangements looking, if possible, to the renunciation of the use and development of the atomic bomb, and directing and encouraging the use of atomic energy and all future scientific information toward peaceful and humanitarian ends. . . . I therefore propose to initiate discussions, first with our associates in this discovery, Great Britain and Canada, and then with other nations, in an effort to effect agreement on the conditions under which co-operation might replace rivalry in the field of atomic power." Prophetically, the President commented: "The difficulties in working out such arrangements are great." He might have added that the difficulties in working out a law providing for domestic control were also not small.

On the same day that the President delivered his message on atomic energy to the Congress, an Administration bill providing for domestic control was introduced simultaneously in both Houses. This bill, which had been prepared by the Secretary of War's committee, was introduced in the Senate by Senator Edwin Johnson and in the House by Representative Andrew May, chairman of the House Military Affairs Committee. It became known as the May-Johnson Bill, and it provided for a part-time Atomic Energy Commission to which Army and Navy officers on active duty could be appointed. The bill gave the Commission great powers and considerable latitude on how it was to exercise them.

Almost as soon as the May-Johnson Bill had been introduced, a great controversy broke out in the Congress and across the land on the issue of civilian versus military control of atomic energy. In the hot debate which followed, the May-Johnson Bill became the symbol of military control. It was attacked from many powerful quarters, notably by the scientists who had been connected with the wartime program. In a highly unusual invasion of the political arena the scientists organized themselves into a forceful pressure group that went to work to insure the civilian control of atomic energy in the United States.

In acknowledgment of the controversy which raged around the May-Johnson Bill, the Senate on October 29 appointed a Special Committee on Atomic Energy, with Senator McMahon as its chairman, to make "a full, complete and continuing study and investigation with respect to problems relating to the development, use and control of atomic energy." This Committee began hearings the next month, and on December 20 Senator McMahon introduced his second bill, which became the basis for hearings which continued until the following April. This bill provided for a full-time Commission whose members were to be allowed no conflicting military or business interests. It also spelled out in considerable detail how the Commission was to exercise its enormous powers, and created a government monopoly in the field of atomic energy. Just as the May-Johnson Bill had become the symbol of military control, the McMahon Bill became the symbol of civilian control, and the scientists adopted it as their standard. So did President Truman, who in February wrote a letter to Senator McMahon calling for legislation essentially along the lines of the McMahon Bill.

In the discussions which proceeded through the winter and spring of 1946, both within and without the hearing-room of the Senate's Special Committee on Atomic Energy, some basic areas of agreement began to emerge. Everybody seemed to believe that the atom should be rigidly controlled by the government; everybody seemed to believe that this control should be exercised by civilians, and everybody seemed to believe that the military services should have a voice in the atomic energy program short of control.

Ultimately it became clear that the only point of disagreement remaining was that of determining the precise limits of military participation. In an effort to compromise this issue, Senator Vandenberg proposed an amendment to the McMahon Bill which would provide for the establishment of a Military Liaison Committee to work with the Commission on atomic energy matters of military interest. But the proponents of civilian control found the powers this amendment bestowed upon the Liaison Committee to be far too great, and once again reacted violently. Thus the compromise had to be compromised. A final version of the Vandenberg Amendment was eventually hammered out, however, and the McMahon Bill, after a debate in the House which led to a strengthening of the security provisions, passed both Houses of Congress in its final form in July and was signed into law by the President on August 1, 1946.

The new law, called the Atomic Energy Act of 1946, established a five-man Atomic Energy Commission, whose members were to be appointed by the President with the advice and consent of the Senate, and who were specifically prevented from engaging "in any other business, vocation or employment than that of serving as a member of the Commission."

The law bestowed enormous powers on the Commission, and furthermore ordered it to use them. For example, the Commission was required to own all the materials from which atomic energy can be produced, all the facilities in which such materials can be manufactured, and all the patents related to the production and use of such materials. In addition, the law directed the Commission to control through licenses and regulations all the minerals from which atomic energy materials could be produced, and all information related to atomic energy. It also directed the Commission to conduct an extensive atomic research program, and authorized it, at the direction of the President, to develop and produce atomic weapons. In other words, the law gave the Atomic Energy Commission a monopoly in the field of atomic energy, with the right to control all vital activities through direct ownership and management, and all other activities by means of regulations and licenses. To help the Commission protect its secrets, the Congress provided for some stiff penalties for violations of the law, extending even to death or life imprisonment. The law also ended

all co-operation with Britain and Canada in the important
fields of weapons and atomic power.

As a guide to the Commission in the exercise of its great
powers, a declaration of over-all policy was included in
the law which illustrates perhaps better than anything
else Congress' awareness of the fateful decision it had
made when it set the course of atomic energy control and
development in the United States. "It is hereby declared
to be the policy of the people of the United States," the
Act says, "that, subject at all times to the paramount
objective of assuring the common defense and security,
the development and utilization of atomic energy shall,
so far as practicable, be directed toward improving the
public welfare, increasing the standard of living, strengthening free competition in private enterprise, and pro-
moting world peace."

To encourage and assist the Commission to exercise
its great powers prudently and wisely, the law established
a Joint Congressional Committee on Atomic Energy,
composed of nine Senators and nine Representatives, and
specified that the Commission "shall keep the Committee fully and currently informed with respect to the
Commission's activities." It also established a nine-
member General Advisory Committee, to be appointed by
the President "from civilian life," to advise the Commission on scientific and technical matters, and the Military
Liaison Committee provided for by the Vandenberg
Amendment. The Liaison Committee, which is appointed
by the Secretary of Defense, consists of two representatives from each of the three armed services plus a chairman who may be either a military man or a civilian. The
Commission is directed by the law to "advise and consult
with the Committee on all atomic energy matters which
the Committee deems to relate to military applications"
and to "keep the Committee fully informed of all such

matters before it." The Committee, on the other hand, is instructed to "keep the Commission fully informed of all atomic energy matters" in the Defense Department. The Committee furthermore is given the right to make written recommendations to the Commission and to appeal disputes through the Secretary of Defense to the President.

Thus it was that America's approach to the postwar atom was established on the home front. In essence, the approach was one of rigid government control, this control to be administered by civilian officials. Assurance of the national defense and security was established as the principal goal, but it was also made clear that the newly reconstituted program was expected to work toward realization of the peaceful promise of atomic energy insofar as possible. By mid-1946, then, the domestic course had been set. All that remained was to name the people who would control the new program and to arrange for the transfer of the property and people of the Manhattan District to the newly established Commission.

Meanwhile, the American position on the international front had also been set, and there was still some hope in the world that it, or something like it, might be put into effect. By mid-1946 also, an Atomic Energy Commission had been established in the United Nations at the instigation of the United States, Great Britain, and Canada, joined by Russia, China, and France, and an American plan for international control had been developed and proposed to this Commission. This plan, like the domestic plan, relied upon direct management as the only really effective means of control. In essence, the plan called for the creation of an "International Atomic Development Authority" with power to manage directly all dangerous atomic energy activities in all nations, to conduct a research and development program in the peaceful applications of atomic energy, and to exercise loose control over all non-dangerous activities. The plan also called for a system of inspection to prevent clandestine activities by national governments, and a system of enforcement. If such a plan were set up, the United States offered to dispose of its atomic bombs, give up all its activities in the weapons field, and turn over all of its atomic energy knowledge to the international agency.

The basis for this plan was developed in the State Department in January, February, and March of 1946 by a Committee composed of Undersecretary of State Dean Acheson as chairman, and Vannevar Bush, James B. Conant, General Leslie R. Groves, and John J. McCloy as members. The Committee had the assistance of a Board of Consultants of which David E. Lilienthal was chairman and Chester I. Barnard, J. Robert Oppenheimer, Charles Allen Thomas, and Harry A. Winne were members. The report issued by the Committee in March became known as the Acheson-Lilienthal Report, and it formed the basis of the American proposal made by the American Delegate Bernard Baruch to the United Nations Atomic Energy Commission on June 14, 1946. It was in this historic address that Mr. Baruch prefaced his remarks with the now famous declaration: "We are here to make a choice between the quick and the dead."

The world now knows what happened to that proposal. Six months later something substantially the same was reported to the Security Council as the majority plan of the United Nations Commission, but it has never been adopted. And neither has any of its modified successors, solely because the Russians and their puppets have not agreed with the majority of the members of the United Nations Atomic Energy Commission. The Russians have said that they would consider such a plan to constitute an unwarranted invasion of their national sovereignty. They have also said that they would prefer to destroy all of the world's atomic weapons first and have them renounced as weapons of war, and then talk about how atomic energy might be controlled. The majority, for its part, has rejected these somewhat unrealistic proposals on the grounds that they provide no safeguards against the surreptitious accumulation of a vast stockpile of bombs. But all this has been but a symptom, not the cause, of the basic sickness in the world, a sickness that has led to the cold war between the East and West, the hot war in Korea and Indo-China, and the atomic armaments race between the United States and the Soviet Union. As a result of this cold war and this armaments race, the American atomic energy program has been largely a weapons program carried on in secrecy and with the utmost urgency. Progress has been made on the peaceful side, but, in the language of the law, it has never been the "paramount objective."

It was at midnight on December 31, 1946, that the newly established Commission took over the American atomic energy program from the Army's Manhattan District. The Commission's inheritance included:

1. Facilities with a capital investment of approximately $1,400,000,000, including a weapons research laboratory and a town of about 9,000 people at Los Alamos, New Mexico; important production plants, a research laboratory, and a town of about 36,000 people at Oak Ridge, Tennessee; an important production plant and a town of about 17,000 at Hanford, Washington; a temporarily housed research laboratory in Chicago; some important research equipment at the Radiation Laboratory in Berkeley, California; and research laboratories then under construction at Brookhaven, Long Island; Schenectady, New York; and Miamisburg, Ohio.

2. A program that had about 5,000 direct government employees, both military and civilian, and about 50,000 contractor employees.

3. A system under which virtually all of the scientific

and industrial work was performed by private contractors. There were several hundred research contractors, several score important industrial contractors, and several thousand suppliers, performers of special services, and subcontractors of various sorts.

4. The knowledge of how to produce atomic bombs.

The new Commission very early decided to do its business, as the Manhattan District had done, through private scientific and industrial contractors, confining itself to policy direction and administrative supervision of the work. This served two purposes: it made available to the Commission the management and technical skills of American industry and science, and at the same time it served to spread knowledge about atomic energy through the American economy. It also made it possible for the Commission to hold down the number of direct government employees. Today, although the program has been expanded several times in size over what it was in 1947, the number of direct Commission employees has increased from 5,000 to but 7,000. Meanwhile, the number of contractor employees has increased from 50,000 to nearly 200,000.

To carry out the responsibilities vested in it by the Atomic Energy Act, the Commission is organized roughly along the lines of a private corporation. At the top, where policy is set, are the five Commissioners. Next in line is the chief executive officer, called the General Manager. Originally the General Manager was appointed by the President; he is now appointed by and is directly responsible to the five Commissioners. Below the General Manager are a number of operating divisions, each with its own responsibility, such as military applications, production, research, reactor development, biology and medicine, and security. Most of the Commission's day-to-day relations with its contractors are through field offices located at Oak Ridge, Hanford, New York, Chicago,

Albuquerque, and wherever else there is a major atomic energy activity.

The Commission's first Chairman was David E. Lilienthal, former head of the Tennessee Valley Authority and co-author of the Acheson-Lilienthal Report which formed the basis of the American plan for the international control of atomic energy. He served until his resignation on February 15, 1950, and was succeeded by the author, who occupied the office of Chairman from July 11, 1950, until his resignation in June 30, 1953. From February 15 to July 11, 1950, the Commission functioned under the acting chairmanship of Sumner T. Pike, one of the original members of the Commission. Besides Mr. Pike, who had been a New England businessman and former Federal Power Commissioner, the original Commission was composed of the New York businessman and former Rear Admiral Lewis L. Strauss, the atomic scientist Robert F. Bacher, and the Iowa publisher William W. Waymack. As the years passed the composition of the Commission gradually changed, and by February 1952 it consisted of the atomic scientist Henry de Wolfe Smyth, the New York businessman and engineer Thomas E. Murray, the former Air Force Assistant Secretary Eugene M. Zuckert, the Ohio educator and engineer T. Keith Glennan, and the author. All of the last-named, with the exception of Mr. Glennan, who resigned November 1, 1952, remain as members of the Commission at this writing.

For most of the more than six years that the Commission has been in existence, the Joint Congressional Committee on Atomic Energy functioned under the chairmanship of the author of the Atomic Energy Act, the late Senator Brien McMahon, and the General Advisory Committee functioned under the chairmanship of the scientist given the most credit for developing the atomic bomb, Dr. J. Robert Oppenheimer. These men and their colleagues, like those who have served on the Commission itself, have done much to determine the scope and shape of the American atomic energy program as it exists today.

But this is not a book about personalities. It is not even a book about the Commission. It is, instead, a book about the atomic energy program itself, a program that has been driven forward and expanded under a great sense of urgency as the only means by which the free world might compensate for the collapse of the great expectations once held for international control. Mr. Baruch in 1946 gave the world a choice between the quick and the dead. That choice has not yet been made, but time has been bought in which it might yet be made correctly, and it has been bought largely through the effort described in the following pages of this book.

# CHAPTER ii

# *Uranium Is Where You Find It*

Man has just begun to look for uranium. Only a few years ago it was an unimportant metal used almost exclusively as a ceramic coloring agent. No one cared much about it. Today it is the essential feed material for the great atomic energy plants of this and other countries. It is the base of the atomic energy pyramid and—it is hard to find.

It is almost as though some wise Providence, distrustful of man's wisdom, had hidden it out. For example, uranium from the famed Shinkolobwe Mine in the Belgian Congo must travel twelve hundred miles before it reaches a seaport and must then make a much longer ocean journey before it reaches the United States. It was hidden—at least, not discovered—until 1915. Similarly, uranium from Canada's Great Bear Lake must travel fifteen hundred miles from its source—twenty-five miles from the Arctic Circle —before it reaches a railroad, and it can make this journey through icy waters but a few months of the year. Providence kept the secret of this deposit until 1930.

Such uranium as has been found in the United States is deposited for the most part in the sandstone of the Colorado plateau. Far back in geological history this uranium was probably brought to the surface by volcanic action or the boiling up of hot ashes and liquids from the restless depths of the earth. Over the ages, many of the rocks in which the uranium was deposited have been worn away, and much of the uranium itself has been dissipated. Some of it, however, by a mechanism not thoroughly understood, has been concentrated in tiny, inaccessible pockets in the desert sandstone. The first uranium was found on the plateau at the turn of the century, but an intensive search is still going on to discover all of the places where the pocket deposits have been hidden away.

One could hardly expect prospectors to burn up much energy or bankers to dig very deeply into their pockets simply to locate a mineral that up to World War II was used mainly as a coloring agent for porcelain and stained glass—and they didn't. But in 1898 something happened that spurred the search for uranium deposits. Radium was discovered by Mme Curie in Paris. The connection between uranium and radium is that uranium always contains an infinitesimal amount of radium—about one part in three million—and, with radium selling at $200,000 per gram, the search in all parts of the world was frantic.

One of the richest uranium-radium deposits was discovered at Joachimsthal, in Bohemia. The Joachimsthal area has a colorful past. It also has an active present and future, for it is today under the control of the Russians. Let's have a look at it before we return to some of the uranium deposits on this side of the Iron Curtain.

In both Saxony, which is today a part of Russian Germany, and Bohemia, which is today a part of Russian Czechoslovakia, there is an extremely rich mineral region. It is located in the Erzgebirge range, which separates the two countries. The region has been mined since the latter part of the twelfth century. Originally mining operations centered on the tin field of Schönfeld. In the sixteenth century, however, interest turned from tin to silver, and the mining activity shifted to Joachimsthal. Silver mining proved so successful that a mint was established where

silver coins, called *Joachimsthaler*, were struck. The word
*Joachimsthaler* was later contracted to *Thaler*, a name
that is still used for certain coins in various parts of the
world and, incidentally, is the root of the American word
*dollar*.

Three hundred years later the mines of Joachimsthal
turned up a little-known mineral, pitchblende, in heavy
blue-black veins containing uranium. Uranium had come
into demand because of its use as a coloring agent. The
mines flourished. With the discovery of radium at the turn
of the last century, international attention was again focused on the mines, which for a period enjoyed a world
monopoly in that elusive and extremely costly element.

Today some of the most productive pitchblende mines
in the fabulous Erzgebirge range are located at Joachimsthal. There are three of them. One characteristic of the
mines is that silver is particularly plentiful in the upper
workings. At the middle levels, however, one finds cobalt,
nickel, and bismuth. The pitchblende ore with its uranium
is found most abundantly in the lower workings. Although the richest ore was probably taken out long ago,
thousands of slave laborers are today fervently scratching
away in these lower levels, extracting the remaining ore
to feed the Russian atomic effort. Additional thousands
are busy in the many mines of Saxony where there is an
apparently plentiful supply of lower grade ore. What
kind of effort all this goes to support will be discussed in
a later chapter.

There is one striking similarity among the uranium-
bearing ores of the world's three most famous deposits:
the Joachimsthal, the Shinkolobwe, and the Canadian
deposits of the Great Bear Lake. In each the ore is the
high-grade source of uranium, pitchblende, and it is
found in association with cobalt and nickel and certain
other base and precious metals.

Unfortunately, the United States is a have-not nation

world's richest uranium mine. He must know also that there are people behind such an operation, courageous and friendly men like Edgar Sengier of the Union Minière, men who deal in "blue chips" but who have yet never haggled when the defense of the Western World was the issue. He must be able to picture barges coursing their way south from the Arctic Circle, carrying the ore of the Great Bear Lake, and in so doing he must see that ore being lifted from those barges, trucked across portages to the next waterway, there again to be reloaded. To have any appreciation at all of the problems involved in the search for this elusive metal, he must be able somehow to picture a grizzled prospector in the lonely reaches of the Colorado plateau tapping away at an outcropping somewhere high on a mesa; Congressmen urging on behalf of the miners that the precipitous rocky roads of the region be improved so that they may get their ore to market; miners asserting that the procedure for assaying their samples is unfair; colleges insisting that their scientists be given a grant to work on the problem of extracting uranium from low-grade ore; geologists leaving the Commission's employ when appropriations are cut; diamond drillers insisting that with inflation the price per foot of drilling must be increased; Indians of the Navajo tribe meeting in sober council to work out some arrangement whereby this new birthright discovered on their reservation will not be sold for a mess of pottage.

Yes, one must be able to picture, if even in a very vague fashion, five Commissioners in Washington, D. C., attempting to find a formula whereby an incentive can be provided to explore and mine, without at the same time pouring taxpayers' money down some pack-rat hole in the Western desert. And he must understand the strong and understandable proprietary feeling which prevails in so many countries of the world, such as India and Brazil and Australia, countries which are most reluctant to deplete those natural resources which may someday spell for them great future blessings in terms of cheap power. It seems obvious to me that if we are to continue to get ore from abroad we must be prepared also to give up certain information and equipment and technology which will aid these countries in the development of their own atomic programs. But there will be more on this in the chapter on "The International Atom." Meanwhile, let us see what happens to the ore after it is mined and passes into the hands of the Atomic Energy Commission.

# CHAPTER *iii*

## *The Production Line: Ore to Bombs*

WE have seen where uranium ore comes from and how we go about obtaining it. Now let us see what we do with it after we get it.

It is a long and intricate route that uranium must travel from the mines of the Belgian Congo, northern Canada, South Africa, and the Colorado plateau to the secret locations where atomic bombs are stored. It is also an expensive one.

More than three fourths of all the money and materials and skills that America has invested in her atomic energy program has gone to build up the plants and laboratories that uranium must pass through along the way to a bomb. This is the atomic energy production line. In some ways it is similar to the production lines that lead from the Mesabi iron range of northern Minnesota to your kitchen refrigerator, and from the Texas oil fields to the gasoline tank of your car. But in many other ways it is completely different, unlike anything else that is done in industry and unlike anything else that has ever been done before in the world.

The atomic energy production line includes a myriad industrial processes, ranging all the way from such relatively simple and straightforward operations as the grind-

ing and crushing of ore to the transmutation of elements—
the dream of the ancient alchemists who vainly sought to
change common metals into gold. But the Atomic Energy
Commission is after something far more valuable than
gold. It is after the materials, known to the scientists as
"fissionable," that pack more energy into a pound than
coal does into a thousand tons.

To get these substances the Commission must take ore
that is measured in carload quantities and send it on a
journey from which emerge only minuscule amounts of
material measured in terms of grams. To gain a feeling
for what this journey is like, let us select a particular
quantity, say a ton, of ore and follow it all the way
through—seeing what happens to it and glimpsing the
facilities it passes through along the way.

Let us say that the ore we wish to follow belongs to
you. Let us say you found it high on a mesa in the lonely
distances of the Colorado plateau where a splash of yel-
low among the many hues of that colorful land revealed
the presence of carnotite. Let us say the click of your Gei-
ger counter confirmed your discovery and that you staked
out a claim, just as you would if you found gold or silver
or copper. Although the ore belongs to you—not to the
government—you cannot sell it or give it to anyone except
the Atomic Energy Commission or someone approved by
the Commission.

But there is a good market for your uranium just the
same. The Commission wants it badly, and will buy it
from you even though it contains only two pounds of uranium to each ton of ore.

So you decide to sell your ore to the nearest ore-buying
depot, of which there are fifteen in the Colorado plateau
area operated by either the Commission or one of its contractors. Let us say that the nearest depot to you is the
one at Durango, Colorado, operated by the Vanadium
Corporation of America under Commission contract.

world, fluorine is probably the the most corrosive. It will dissolve glass, severely corrode most metals, including stainless steel, and ignite all organic materials such as wood, clothing, many plastics, and oil. It will even react with water, and if it is introduced into overly moist, confined air, it will explode violently.

Although the process for producing it is a delicate and potentially hazardous one, green salt itself is a stable, relatively harmless compound. It is of very great value to the atomic energy program, for it marks the starting point in the manufacture of both plutonium and uranium-235. It is here, therefore, that the road divides, one fork leading to the bomb stockpiles via the great plutonium plants at Hanford and Savannah River, and the other via the huge uranium-235 plants at Oak Ridge, Paducah, and Portsmouth.

Let us say that half of your uranium goes in one direction and half in the other. On a purely arbitrary basis, for both are important, let us first follow the route marked "plutonium."

To produce plutonium, the material that is needed is pure uranium metal. This metal is rather simply obtained from green salt in one clean chemical operation that removes the fluorine from the salt and leaves pure uranium in a molten blob at the bottom of the reaction vessel. After it has cooled, you can now for the first time see your uranium in all its pristine beauty—a bright, very heavy, hard material not unlike lead in weight and not unlike nickel in color. Your uranium, although mildly toxic if inhaled or eaten in the form of dust, is now safe to touch and hold. And it is not unlike many other metals, such as silver, lead, and gold, except that it will form a grayish-black rust very rapidly along its surface if exposed to the air for any appreciable period of time. When it is recalled that as recently as 1942 there was not enough purified uranium in the world to fill a small briefcase, it is evident that the large-scale production of this metal is no mean achievement.

Now the chemist is through with your uranium for a while, and it passes into the hands of the metallurgist and machinist. Here, with other uranium, it is cast into ingots, rolled into long rods, and then cut into relatively short cylindrical bars. To prevent deterioration through the formation of rust, it is sealed as soon as possible into tight-fitting aluminum cans. It is now ready for the plutonium production plant.

Let us say that one of your two pounds of uranium has found its way into a can destined for one of the futuristic plutonium plants at Hanford on the banks of the majestic Columbia River. The Hanford plant was built during the war by the du Pont Company. It is now operated by General Electric under contract to the Commission.

When it arrives at Hanford your uranium is ready for one of the most exciting and mysterious parts of its journey on the way to a bomb. You can feel the importance and mystery in the air when you visit the government-built town of Richland, which lies just outside the 400,000-acre reservation where the widely separated plutonium plants are located.

Richland is an "open" city. You can drive into it and stay at the hotel. You can walk down its streets, shop in its stores, go to its movies, and visit in its homes. It is a pleasant, busy community of about twenty thousand people, with children playing along its sidewalks, and bakery and laundry trucks mingling with the private cars which line its streets. Except for its freedom from smoke and dirt, it is not unlike many other towns of similar size throughout the country.

But the imprint of the atomic age is upon it just the same. You can feel it when you walk by the white frame building which faces the mall and see the sign in front which says simply: "U.S. Atomic Energy Commission,

Hanford Works." You can feel it when you look out in the direction of the plant area and see the small patrol plane endlessly circling around the periphery of the controlled reservation. And you can feel it when you notice the road leading north, out past the city limits, past the guards and the gate marked "Prohibited Area," and into the barren acreage where the gray shape of one of the plant areas looms faintly in the distance.

It is into this forbidden region that your uranium now must go, there to be transmuted, at least in part, into the precious man-made element plutonium.

The process by which this transmutation is accomplished is unique in industry. It is not a chemical process, such as the burning of coal or the manufacture of synthetic rubber. It is a *nuclear* process and takes place in a huge, box-shaped pile of graphite and uranium which is several stories high and is known, appropriately enough, as a "nuclear reactor."

The reaction which occurs in a nuclear reactor differs from a chemical reaction in that it involves, not such "large" particles of matter as molecules and the outer shells of atoms, but rather the hard, unimaginably minute inner core of an atom known as its nucleus, about which the outer particles revolve as planets around the sun. For a very long time the atom successfully guarded this inner, inviolate area from the increasingly persistent encroachments of man. As a matter of fact, it was only a few years before the advent of the atomic energy program that man first penetrated this inner heart, and even then he was able to do so with only an atom or two at a time, aided by mammoth and ungainly machines bearing such Buck Rogerish names as "cyclotron," "betatron," and "Van de Graaff generator."

This is the world of the Hanford process, of the nuclear chain reaction. It is the world of the proton and neutron, particles of matter so small that more than a hundred million of them would not make a speck large enough for the human eye to see. And it is the world of the physicist and radiochemist—the men of science who ceaselessly probe the mysteries of the nuclei of atoms, and whose researches first produced the knowledge that every so often a uranium-235 nucleus will split in two, releasing neutron "bullets" which, if they can be made to strike other "235" atoms, will in turn cause these to split in two. This is the nuclear chain reaction—the process upon which the entire atomic energy program is built.

It was also the physicist who discovered that these neutron bullets which shoot out a splitting "235" atom will, if they can be made to strike the nucleus of an ordinary uranium atom, called uranium-238, cause it to undergo the miracle of transmutation. In the nuclear reactors at Hanford, billions of such miniature atomic explosions are taking place, and billions upon billions of neutrons are being released to perform their vital work of changing normal uranium into plutonium.

In many ways we can think of this reaction as a nuclear fire. In fact, people who work with reactors often refer to them as nuclear "ovens" in which they "cook" uranium. But the "fire" that is raging inside is not at all like an ordinary coal or chemical fire. For one thing, it needs no oxygen—only neutrons—to make it go. For another, unlike a chemical fire, you can't see or hear it. The billions of miniature explosions are so small and so dispersed among the uranium and graphite that they cannot be detected by any human sense of hearing. But, just like a chemical fire, this nuclear fire produces heat and to keep the reactor from melting, it must constantly be cooled by water flowing through a network of thousands of tiny crevices.

There is another important difference between a nuclear fire and an ordinary chemical one, and that is the production by the nuclear reaction of invisible, intensely lethal rays that must be guarded against by a great shell

do for weapons, we have only to take it out of the bomb stockpile and put it to peaceful use.

You will recall that when we set out on the road marked "plutonium," we left behind approximately a pound of green salt destined to travel the uranium-235 route to a bomb. Now that we have had a glimpse of the plutonium process, let us go back to Fernald and follow this other batch of green salt on its way to a bomb.

The process is quite different. There is, for example, no transmutation involved, and no nuclear reaction. But it is no less unusual, no less fabulous, and no less difficult.

The differences between the two processes stem partly from the fact that uranium-235, unlike plutonium, exists in nature. It is present in all natural uranium, and it is therefore present in the uranium in your green salt. The problem is to get it out.

To acquire some idea of the magnitude of this job, it must first be understood that uranium-235 is an extremely rare substance. Although it exists in natural uranium, it is there in a ratio of only 1 to 140—in other words, there is but one part of "235" to each 140 parts of the normal uranium known as uranium-238.

It must also be understood that uranium-235 is identical, chemically speaking, with uranium-238. This means that it melts at exactly the same temperature, and that it reacts with all chemicals in exactly the same way. Thus, if you were to place a small quantity of "235" in one test tube and an equal quantity of "238" in another, and were to pour in, one at a time, every other substance known to man, the reactions that would take place in each test tube would be identical. As you can see, this poses a rather difficult problem when one wishes to develop an effective means of separating the two.

It was this problem of separation that occupied the attention of a good many of the scientists connected with the Manhattan Engineering District during the war. Because there is no chemical difference between uranium-235 and 238, the scientists quite naturally turned to its nuclear differences to find an effective separation process.

There is, of course, one spectacular nuclear difference between "235" and "238": the nucleus of a "235" atom will split in two when struck by a neutron, whereas the "238" nucleus will change into plutonium. But this is hardly a useful means of separation, for, even if we could shoot a stream of neutron bullets into a piece of uranium, we would succeed only in destroying the "235," not in isolating it.

The only other difference between uranium-235 and 238 that is of any consequence is a very, very slight difference in weight. U-235 is lighter. The scientists seized upon this slight difference in weight as the only hope for devising an effective method of separation. Several possible approaches were followed. One of the first was a process known as electromagnetic separation. This consisted of combining the uranium with another substance to form a gas, then charging the gas electrically, then shooting it in a stream of molecules past a giant magnet. The theory was that the lighter molecules would be deflected ever so slightly more than the heavier ones as they passed the magnet, and thus could be collected separately.

Fantastic as it may sound, this process actually worked, and a $350,000,000 plant was erected at Oak Ridge to carry it out. It is a matter of considerable interest that this plant actually produced the uranium-235 that was used in the first atomic bomb that exploded over Hiroshima in August 1945. This process, however, has since been abandoned, for the very good reason that another process was developed about the same time that turned out to be better and more efficient so far as the production of uranium-235 in relatively large quantities is concerned.

It is this newer process, called "gaseous diffusion," that is still used today in the great plants now built or building at Oak Ridge, Paducah, and Portsmouth, in which the government has invested slightly more than three billion dollars. So far as its basic principle is concerned, the gaseous-diffusion process is not a complicated one. If you know how a sieve works, you know how gaseous diffusion works, for the basic idea is essentially the same. Uranium in gaseous form is simply pumped through a series of "sieves," called barriers, and the lighter atoms of U-235 are gradually concentrated and taken off at the end of the line in virtually pure form. It is not nearly so simple as separating sand from gravel, however, for in the gaseous-diffusion process we are dealing with individual molecules of matter so small that they cannot be seen even with the most powerful microscope. It is these molecules that must be sifted through the barriers, and therefore the holes in the barrier material must be unbelievably small—less than one two-millionth of an inch in diameter. Another complicating factor is that the difference in weight, and therefore in mass, between the molecules of the heavier U-238 and the lighter U-235 is less than one per cent. This means that if you sent your mixture through but one barrier, the increase in the proportion of U-235 present would be so small that it could hardly be measured. The mixture therefore must be sent, not through one barrier, but through thousands, and this is why gaseous-diffusion plants are so large.

It is hard to imagine uranium, one of the heaviest metals in the world, in the form of a gas. Yet it must be made into a gas if it is to be separated, and so, as the first step in the gaseous-diffusion process, the chemist—the "indispensable man" of the atomic energy program—is called upon to put it in gaseous form.

It is rather typical of the perversity of nature in matters of this sort that the only gas that can be used in the gaseous-diffusion process is uranium hexafluoride, which is composed of one part of uranium to each six parts of our old corrosive friend, fluorine. To make "hex," as uranium hexafluoride has come to be known throughout the atomic energy program, the chemist turns to the green salt we left at Fernald when we decided to follow the plutonium route to a bomb.

Green salt, like "hex," is composed of uranium and fluorine, but it contains proportionately more uranium than does "hex." The chemist's problem, then, is to introduce more fluorine into the compound he already has. This job entails all of the difficulties and potential hazards that anyone who handles fluorine must face, and these are compounded by the unpleasant fact that the chemical bonding of the fluorine to the uranium must take place at a high temperature. But the chemist does it just the same, and the product he gets is now ready for the gaseous-diffusion plant.

Let us look for a moment at this product. In making his "hex" the chemist has not only succeeded in producing a material that can be used in the gaseous-diffusion process; he has also produced a material that is nearly as corrosive and as dangerous to handle as either pure fluorine or hydrofluoric acid. Whereas green salt is a relatively docile compound, this is certainly not true of "hex." It will, like pure fluorine, severely corrode and sometimes ignite many metals and all organic materials if it touches them in the presence of air. And yet this is the material that must be fed into the gaseous-diffusion plants at Oak Ridge, Paducah, and Portsmouth. Moreover, the "hex" must be used in the form of a gas, and yet at room temperature it is actually a solid. To make it into a gas, therefore, its temperature must be raised. This means that while it is in the gaseous-diffusion plant it must be kept relatively hot, a condition which adds to its corrosiveness.

It should be clear from this that a gaseous-diffusion plant must incorporate some design features and some materials that are not required in the usual industrial

diameter. But these are the lengths to which man must go to isolate the explosives—and the fuel—of the atomic age.

When your pound of uranium, in the form of "hex," arrives at Oak Ridge, it is into this remarkable system that it is placed. It goes into one of the many compartments as a hot gas, and from there it is cycled and re-cycled through thousands of other compartments and past thousands of barriers until part of it can be drawn off as gas containing virtually pure uranium-235.

This is the way it works: When your "hex" has been inserted into the plant, and after about half of it has passed through the first barrier into the next forward compartment, the remaining half—slightly depleted in "235"—is drawn off and sent backward to a compartment at a lower stage in the chain. This must be done by halves, because if all or too much of the gas in the first compartment were permitted to pass forward to the next stage, the proportion of "235" in the succeeding stage would not increase. The whole purpose of the plant, of course, is to increase that proportion bit by bit.

This backward-forward movement is repeated at each of the thousands of stages in the plant, with each molecule of the "235" gas inching its way gradually forward through the plant, and each molecule of "238" gradually inching its way backward. The net forward movement is so slight that it takes even the "speediest" molecule many months to pass through the entire plant, and the volume of gas at the lowest stage is more than 100,000 times greater than it is at the uppermost, where the uranium-235 "cream" is taken off.

Once out of the plant, the "hex" that is now highly enriched by uranium-235 goes again to the indispensable chemist, who removes the fluorine, leaving, finally, pure uranium-235 metal. This metal looks exactly like normal natural uranium, and, as a matter of fact, it *is* exactly like normal natural uranium—except for two interesting differences: it is ever so slightly lighter; and it will, if brought together into a "critical mass," explode like an atomic bomb.

As with plutonium, the amount of uranium-235 that has emerged from your original ton of ore is but a fraction of an ounce. And also, as with plutonium, this product goes from Oak Ridge deep behind the cloak of secrecy to the places where it is machined and finally stored in atomic bombs.

You will recall that plutonium deteriorates so slowly that only half of it is gone in 24,000 years. In this respect, uranium-235 is even better, for only half of it will be gone in four million years. Like plutonium, then, it is, so far as we are concerned, a stable, permanent material of immense value, for it can be used not only as an explosive in weapons, but also—if it need never be used in weapons—as fuel for atomic power plants. It is therefore, like plutonium, a national resource of very great importance—a guardian of our freedom today, and a real hope for the future.

# CHAPTER *iv*

## *The Expanding Program*

Most people, I feel sure, have no idea how much the atomic energy program has grown in the six years that have passed since the civilian Commission took over from the Army's Manhattan Engineer District. At the big production centers at Oak Ridge and Hanford, originally built during the war, three major expansions have been undertaken. In addition, three more entirely new billion-dollar production plants have been established at Aiken, South Carolina (called the Savannah River plant); Paducah, Kentucky; and Portsmouth, Ohio.

Each of these important expansions has called for new facilities all along the ore-to-weapons chain—at places like Los Alamos and Sandia, established during the war; Fernald, Ohio, where a new feed-materials processing center has been erected; and Eniwetok and Las Vegas, where new weapons-testing ranges have been set up. Add to these the new research and development facilities at such older locations as Oak Ridge, Brookhaven, Argonne, Berkeley, and Schenectady, and such new locations as Miamisburg, Ohio, the reactor testing station in Idaho, and the atomic power laboratory at Pittsburgh, and you will begin to appreciate the scope and rapidity of the atomic energy program's growth.

Because of security restrictions, it is very hard to describe this growth in detail, particularly as it relates to the nation's capacity to produce weapons materials, but a good idea can be obtained by comparing today's $5,000,-000,000 capital investment in atomic energy with the $1,400,000,000 that applied in 1947. When the current construction program is completed, the figure will have climbed to about $9,000,000,000, which well exceeds the combined capital investment of General Motors, U. S. Steel, du Pont, Bethlehem Steel, Alcoa, and Goodyear. It is also interesting to compare these figures with the $366,000,000 cost of the Panama Canal—a project which took ten years to complete. Even taking the devaluation of the dollar into account, the cost of the atomic energy building program over the past six years is about ten times that amount.

Here are some other illustrations of the magnitude of the current construction program:

1. The new plant at Portsmouth will have a gross floor area equaling that of the Pentagon Building and the famed Willow Run bomber plant combined.

2. The concrete required by the Savannah River plant at Aiken is sufficient to lay a sidewalk five feet wide and six inches thick from coast to coast, and the excavation work will turn up enough earth to form a wall ten feet high and six feet wide from Los Angeles to Boston.

3. The three uranium-235 production plants at Oak Ridge, Portsmouth, and Paducah, when completed, will consume more electric power each day than is produced by the Hoover, Grand Coulee, and Bonneville dams plus the entire original TVA system combined—or more than four times the average daily amount used by New York City in 1952.

4. Four times as much structural steel is being used in the Paducah plant as was used in the Chrysler Building in New York.

5. The materials required to build the Savannah River plant would fill a string of railway cars stretching all the way from New York to St. Louis.

6. The labor force currently engaged in atomic energy construction comprises more than 65,000 people, or about five per cent of the total construction force of the nation.

As can be seen, the Commission is engaged in an enormous construction operation, and the problems associated with it are commensurately large. To provide an idea of the scope and variety of these problems, here is a list of the steps that must be taken as the Commission moves into a major expansion program of the type that is now underway:

1. *Determination of the need.*

The most recent expansion program will ultimately cost over $4,000,000,000. Obviously this is not the sort of undertaking that can be entered into lightly or without thorough study based on hard facts.

The idea that an expansion program is needed may originate from any one of several different reasons: Russian progress, an increase in the availability of uranium, or a new scientific development promising new military uses for atomic energy. But whichever single factor motivates the expansion, all are taken into account before construction work is actually begun, and the final decision invariably involves a good many agencies of government besides the AEC. The Defense and State departments, the Office of Defense Mobilization, the National Security Council, the Bureau of the Budget, the President, and the Congress, all participate in these important national policy decisions.

2. *Determination of the size.*

Here is a typical example of how the size of a major expansion is determined. Commission research produces the likelihood that a variety of new weapons can be developed. This is reported to the Department of Defense, which then evaluates its need for these new weapons in the light of its current war plans, the international situation, and the rate of progress, as we know it, of the Russians.

While this Defense Department evaluation is under way, the Commission looks into the technical and economic feasibility of expanding the program and roughly establishes the upper limits that it believes can be accomplished. This involves an exhaustive study of the foreseeable uranium ore supply and an intensive investigation—with the Office of Defense Mobilization—of the availability of key materials and man power in relation to other defense needs. The Defense Department then presents a statement concerning the additional weapons required, and the Commission states whether or not in its judgment this goal is technically and economically feasible. The size of the proposed expansion, therefore, is determined jointly by the Atomic Energy Commission and the Department of Defense. Throughout the development of these plans, which generally takes several months, the Commission's General Advisory Committee and the Joint Congressional Committee on Atomic Energy are kept fully informed, and their views are given great weight.

3. *Proving the need.*

The undertaking of a major expansion is clearly an important step in the development of the nation's over-all security plans. Once the Commission and the Department of Defense agree jointly on an expansion goal, therefore, the whole idea is reviewed by the Atomic Energy Committee of the National Security Council in order to determine whether it conforms with broad national policy. In addition to the Chairman of the AEC and the Secretary of Defense, this committee also includes the Secretary of State, thus assuring that the expansion coincides with our foreign policy objectives and with the State Department's current estimate of the international situation.

After the NSC's Atomic Energy Committee has reviewed the expansion plan, it goes to the full Council for approval. The Council consists of the President, the Vice President, the Secretary of State, the Secretary of Defense, together with such other high officials as the President may name to it. In its deliberations on atomic energy expansion matters, the Council usually hears reports from the Chairman of the AEC, the Director of the Office of Defense Mobilization, and the members of the Joint Chiefs of Staff. After the Council approves the expansion plan, it goes to the President for his final approval. If he in turn approves it, the important job of explaining the need for the expansion to the Congress begins.

4. *Securing Congressional approval.*

This involves, first of all, working closely with the Budget Bureau to determine the exact dollar amounts that will be needed to get the program under way. Once this is done, the President sends his request for these funds to the House of Representatives, and the Commission prepares to go before the Appropriations Committee of the House to justify the request. During these hearings, which frequently run for several days, the Committee looks into the over-all need for the expansion and examines the individual budget items included in it.

The House can do one of several things to a budget request: It can deny it, approve it, or cut it. It usually cuts it, frequently by ten to fifteen per cent, and sometimes more, apparently on the theory that the Commission is asking for something it really needs, but that it is probably asking for more money than is necessary to accomplish it. Curiously enough, for reasons I will describe in the next chapter the Commission frequently asks for too little.

If the Congress, for good reasons, makes cuts on specific items in the budget, the Commission can understand that and can discuss intelligently with the appropriate committees the precise effect these cuts will have. But across-the-board cuts of a fixed percentage are hard to understand, hard to live with, and hard to rebut with specific data. Yet, too frequently this is the kind of a cut that is made.

After the House has acted on the budget request, it goes to the Senate, where more hearings are held before the Senate Appropriations Committee. If there is a difference between the appropriations bills as finally passed by the House and Senate, as there frequently is, this difference is resolved by a Joint Conference Committee. Then the appropriations bill, representing Congressional authorization for the expansion, is passed by both Houses of Congress and sent to the President for approval. If he signs it, then, and not until then, is the Commission in business.

I think it is pertinent to note what happened to the last big expansion program the Commission took to the Congress—the one currently under way and which involves the new plant at Portsmouth, among other important new construction. The Congress approved that program, but by the very narrowest of margins. The program will ultimately cost something over $4,000,000,000. To enter into the necessary contracts and get it started, we needed roughly $3,000,000,000 the first year. We consequently asked for that amount, and we asked for it at a bad time—just before the political conventions in Chicago last summer and toward the end of the Congressional session. We would have preferred to wait for quieter times, but the urgency of the expansion was such that we felt the nation could not afford to wait.

When we presented our case to the House Appropriations Committee, this is what I said:

"We are well aware that this is no ordinary request for funds.

"We know that it involves a very large sum of money—

the largest single sum ever requested for the national atomic energy program.

"We know, too, that it involves a very large construction effort that will inevitably make heavy demands upon many critical materials that are in short supply.

"And we know that it comes at a time when other defense expenditures are extremely high. . . .

"And yet we have concluded that this request must be made. As a matter of fact, we strongly believe—on the basis of all the information we have had—that we would be grossly derelict in the discharge of our responsibility if we failed to make it, and if we failed to make it at this time. . . .

"The setting in which this request is made stems from recent revolutionary developments in the field of atomic weapons technology. Through these developments, the whole concept of how atomic weapons can be utilized in warfare has been radically revised.

"No longer are they looked upon only as devices to be used in an 'Hiroshima-type' way against cities and industrial areas. It is now possible to have a complete 'family' of atomic weapons, for use not only by strategic bombers, but also by ground-support aircraft, armies and navies.

"The Department of Defense is very much aware of this change in concept, and atomic weapons are being incorporated into the operational plans of all three of the armed services.

"This, quite naturally, has greatly increased the demand for atomic weapons—to an entirely different order of magnitude than obtained a few years ago.

"It is the purpose of this expansion to meet this new demand and to meet it as soon as possible.

"We could, of course, meet this demand eventually with the facilities we now have on hand or building. But we would meet it much later. This new expansion is designed to reach the minimum military stockpile requirement at least four, and possibly five, years earlier than would otherwise be the case—four years in which we can be sure the Soviet Union will not be idle."

The House, after debating the need for this expansion and agreeing that it was necessary, then proceeded to cut the appropriations request severely—back to $1,450,000,-000, or about half the amount we had determined we would need for the first year. Furthermore, the House inserted a rider which said that we could not start any construction project for which we did not have the money we would need to complete it. This meant we could start only part of the program. In fact, it meant we could start only a very small fraction of it, because the whole program was so highly integrated that it either had to be started *in toto* or not at all. We could, of course, have taken our $1,450,-000,000 and gone back and devised an entirely new expansion program costing that amount (which would have taken months more to work out), but it would have been a different kind of program, and it would not have reached the weapons goals by anywhere near the date the President, the National Security Council, the Department of Defense, and the Commission had determined to be necessary.

We therefore went to the Senate and explained our reasoning. We told the Senate Committee that we could get along with the heavy reduction in dollars if we could only have relief from the restrictive rider. We figured that if we could use the $1,450,000,000 to begin projects we could pay for with money to be obtained later, we could get under way. The President also sent a strong letter to the Senate asking for the same relief. The Senate agreed with us and instructed its members on the Joint Conference Committee to try to eliminate the rider.

But the House remained adamant, and the Conference Committee sent back a report with the rider still in it.

This the Senate, after a historic and dramatic debate lasting over the Fourth of July week end, rejected by the very narrowest of margins. The vote was actually a tie—34 to 34—which meant that the report was not adopted.

The Conference Committee went back to work, and, after a series of compromises, we finally ended with the rider after all—but with $2,898,000,000 instead of the $1,450,000,000 we had originally been given. This was the minimum amount we needed to get the program started as long as the rider remained in force, and we began putting it to good use as soon the President signed the appropriations bill.

Thus the Congress, while refusing to give up on the principle of the rider, nevertheless gave us the money we needed to overcome its restrictive effect. It was a curious result to a stirring, nonpartisan legislative battle, and one that I would never have predicted in advance. But we were satisfied with the result because we were given what we needed. I can't say, however, that the train of events leading to this result did anything to add to our equanimity.

5. *Decision on whether to build a new site.*

Very early in the development of plans for a new expansion the Commission must decide whether it would be best to enlarge existing plants or to build new ones. Normally, one would think, it would be cheaper and simpler to enlarge existing facilities than to establish new locations. But this is not always the wisest and most practical thing to do, and there may be any number of reasons why this is the case.

One of these reasons involves power. Gaseous-diffusion plants, such as those at Oak Ridge, Paducah, and Portsmouth, use tremendous quantities of electric power. Usually, to meet this demand, new power plants must be erected in the same utility region as the Commission's plant. But it turns out that you can build a gaseous-diffusion plant slightly faster than you can build a power plant. This means that the Commission makes very heavy temporary power demands upon existing power facilities in the area where it is building. Frequently an area where the Commission already has a large plant cannot meet this interim power demand, and this makes it necessary to go to another part of the country. In addition, the Commission has tried to be careful about developing the power resources of any single region beyond the point where the power can be absorbed if for one reason or another the atomic energy program ever goes out of business. If the Commission has reached this point in one region, therefore, it has felt that it should move on to another when a big new expansion came along.

Another reason involves vulnerability. As a general rule, the Commission has felt it would be highly unwise to put all of its production eggs in one or two over-sized baskets that could easily be knocked out in time of war. It wants more than one production line moving from the ore fields to the bomb stockpiles. In this way it can keep any single target from becoming uniquely attractive, and thus have a better chance of keeping the production line flowing in case of atomic attack.

There are other important factors to be taken into account in deciding whether a new site is necessary. If the expansion, for example, involves building a new plant incorporating an entirely new process, with new and different types of supporting facilities, as the Savannah River plant entails, then the plant is built at a new site. Also, if there is a good deal of construction work already under way at an established site which any new work would interfere with, then serious consideration is given to going elsewhere.

Another important reason involves efficiency. The Commission has felt that there is an optimum size to an atomic energy facility beyond which management efficiency tends

addition, a number of smaller facilities, such as those at Rocky Flats and Boulder, Colorado, and Camp Ellis, Illinois, have had to be established at new locations.

Site selection is often a long, trying, time-consuming operation. It took five months, for example, to find just the right location for the Savannah River plant at Aiken, and nine months to turn up the right place for the Portsmouth plant. As can be seen, this site selection process in some cases must begin many months before Congressional authorization for the expansion is obtained. Otherwise, long delays in getting construction under way would be incurred. The Commission's objective has always been to be ready to award contracts within days or weeks after final approval is given to an expansion, and this has meant that the site selection process has had to go on concurrently with most of the other steps leading up to actual construction.

The Commission tries to carry on these site selection studies as quietly as possible, partly because it doesn't want the Russians to know a new expansion is being planned until the last possible moment; partly because, until Congress acts, it is never a sure bet that the expansion will actually be undertaken; and partly because innocent people might otherwise be hurt by land speculation. It is hard for speculators to hurt the government, because the government can always resort to condemnation at a fair price, but this right cannot be used to protect the private citizens who own property adjacent to our reservation.

It is very hard, however, with survey parties traveling around the countryside and with teams of experts poring over records in city halls and talking to chambers of commerce, local officials, and labor unions, for the AEC to keep secret for very long the fact that it is in the market for a new site. But it tries as long as it can, and it generally succeeds for a period of several months. Eventually, however, in every case the news must become public, and then begins the deluge of contacts from people who either want the new plant very badly or who just as strongly hope we will locate it somewhere else. These people approach the President, the Congress, and the Commission.

During our effort to find a suitable location for the plant ultimately located at Portsmouth, we received more than seven hundred letters from Chambers of Commerce, public officials, labor organizations, and individuals, and a score of personal visits by delegations from various cities. These were divided about equally between those who wanted the plant and those who didn't. Most of the people who wanted the plant wanted it because they needed new industry, and consequently new employment and business opportunities in their area. Most of the others were opposed to the plant because of an already tight labor situation, because they thought it would increase their attractiveness as a bomb target, because of a housing shortage, or because the plant would be located in a region attractive as a farming or residential area. Portsmouth, Ohio, where the plant was finally located, wanted it very badly. No one kept a record of the number of phone calls we received about the location of this plant, but I am sure they exceeded the number of letters and personal visits.

When we were looking for a site for the Savannah River plant we received well over six hundred letters or personal visits, mostly from people wanting the plant. How many the Congress and the President received, I don't know, but I do know that President Truman must have received a good many, for at the height of the interest in the plant location problem, on August 19, 1950, he sent me the following note:

TO THE CHAIRMAN, ATOMIC ENERGY COMMISSION

I've had delegations from Arkansas, Missouri and several other States in regard to new locations for atomic energy plants. This is a matter the Atomic Energy Commission itself will have to settle.

I hope you will place these plants where they will be most useful for the objective you are trying to obtain and that you will allow no pressure groups of any sort to influence you in their location.

/s/  HST

Although I hope it is needless to say so, I would like to emphasize that the Commission has never allowed any outside pressures of any sort to influence it in the selection of a location for a new plant, with one possible exception: It has taken into consideration, and I think necessarily and legitimately so, the over-all attitude of the residents in the various areas it has had under consideration for certain plants. If this local attitude has been unanimously, or nearly unanimously, against location of the plant in that area, and if the reasons put forward are good ones, the Commission has taken this fact into account in its deliberations—but even then only if all other factors are equal. It attaches some importance to this local attitude, however, because it can see that a generally unfriendly reaction could easily cause delays, headaches, and added expense that might adversely affect the total program later on.

But there are so many other technical and administrative factors affecting the location of a new plant that the Commission would soon find itself with some rather horrible mistakes on its hands if it for a moment permitted selfish outside interests to influence its final selection decision. Here are some of the principal factors which *do* govern the selection of new sites:

1. *Vulnerability.*

According to military authorities, some sections of the country are more vulnerable to foreign attack than others. The Commission therefore tries to locate its facilities in the least vulnerable areas. Also, within this preferred zone, it is in the interest of national security to keep vital defense industries and facilities as widely dispersed as possible.

2. *Power.*

This is especially important in the selection of sites for gaseous-diffusion plants, which use fantastic amounts of electrical power. As a result, these plants must be built in areas where the sources of power are plentiful and cheap. Most of the power used in the AEC's gaseous-diffusion plants comes from coal, so you will find the plants invariably located in areas where coal is available in large quantities and at low cost. Oak Ridge's power comes from TVA; Paducah's partly from TVA and partly from a private utility network in the Illinois-Missouri-Kentucky area; and Portsmouth's comes from a private utility network in the Ohio-West Virginia-Indiana area. Power is not quite such a controlling item in the location of plutonium production plants, but it is still very important.

3. *Water.*

A large supply of fresh water is a controlling factor in the location of the production facilities (Hanford and Savannah River) which use nuclear reactors. Both the plant at Hanford, located on the Columbia River, and the Savannah River plant in South Carolina use more water daily than a city of over a million people. Adequate supplies of water are also important to the operation of gaseous-diffusion plants, which explains why Oak Ridge is on the Clinch River, Paducah is on the Ohio, and the Portsmouth plant is on the Scioto, just north of the Ohio.

4. *Terrain.*

Plants as large as the AEC's big production facilities require a terrain that is relatively level and free from such construction impediments as rocks, ravines, and an excessive amount of trees. The area and its approaches must also be free from flooding.

The Commission has tried to compensate for at least some of the inadequacies of the CPFF contract system by employing only companies with first-class reputations that would be damaged if they did not do a first-class, cost-conscious job. The list of major operating and construction contractors to the Commission is a virtual blue book of American industry. These concerns take a real pride in their atomic energy work, and they have a strong desire not to do anything that might hurt the fine reputations they have earned over the course of many years.

One might think that there would be real enthusiasm on the part of industry for a type of contract by which the government assumed the whole risk and the contractor was paid a fee besides. In actual practice, however, this is not the case. No matter how much we might hear about the potential extravagance of the CPFF-type contract, there is no great desire on the part of industry to work under it. The reason is that the fee, which is fixed in advance (it does not increase if costs go up), is simply not large enough to compensate most of our contractors for the resources they must assign to our work.

Why, then, are they willing to work for the Commission under this kind of contract? From my own experience, I would say there are three principal reasons:

1. *Sincere patriotism:* the desire to do something to enhance the national security.

2. *The ground-floor motivation:* the desire to gain valuable know-how through experience that can be applied later on for profit when atomic energy may no longer be a government monopoly.

3. *Prestige:* the desire for the recognition that important pioneering work in a promising new industry can bring.

These reasons, of course, affect each of the Commission's contractors in varying degree, but I am sure that one or the other of them is present in nearly every case. In any event, it appears obvious that it is not the fee alone that motivates most of these companies. In some cases the fee is nothing more than a nominal amount, ranging downward to as little as $1.00 per year. In other cases, no fee at all is paid—just the expenses of the job.

Even so, both the government and industry would rather see the CPFF-type contract replaced entirely by a unit price or lump-sum type which would help shift the atomic energy industry over to a more competitive base where initiative and efficiency would be rewarded in terms of profit. But the pioneering nature of the work, the great size of the projects involved, and the need for speed preclude this in many cases, at least for the time being.

Another headache stemming from these same factors can readily be seen when one remembers that the Commission must obtain the money for these projects from the Congress, and that the Congress quite reasonably wants to know just exactly how much something is going to cost before appropriating the funds. And yet in many cases the Commission simply cannot say with any real assurance. If it waited until all of the final design work was done and then asked the Congress for the money, literally months, and sometimes years, would be lost in the process—years in which the Russian atomic energy program, we can be sure, would keep on building. And if designs were arbitrarily frozen before construction was completed, the Commission would probably find its hands tied when it wanted to incorporate a newly discovered improvement that would greatly increase production efficiency.

What the Commission must do, then, in most cases is to give the Congress its best guess as to the final cost when it submits its request for funds. Understandably enough, this usually doesn't satisfy the appropriations committees, however. Sometimes the Commission overestimates, and subsequently saves money that is returned to the federal treasury. Most of the time, however, it underestimates.

I have often wondered just why it is that the cost-estimate errors a design engineer makes are usually on the under side. The law of averages would suggest that over a long period of time the errors would tend to equalize, so that eventually total costs would figure out about as anticipated. But this isn't the case. Even allowing for the inflationary factor which has been at work in recent years, estimates of costs too frequently come out too low. I suppose the real reason is the human element—the tendency always to be just a trifle optimistic. If you have ever tried to plan a household budget in advance, or to allocate a fixed amount to a vacation trip, I think you will understand what the Commission is up against. And when the Commission succeeds in overcoming this tendency it frequently crops up again in the Budget Bureau, which must approve each of the Commission's budget items before they go to the Congress.

Perhaps the most erroneous "guesstimate" the Commission has made—and certainly the largest dollarwise—had to do with the great Savannah River plant now building in South Carolina. This plant involves a new process never before used; construction started long before the design work was more than ten-per-cent complete; many improvements have been incorporated as construction has progressed, and the size of the project has been substantially increased. But the Congress, understandably, wanted to know how much this plant was finally going to cost before we started to work on it. At that time—in December 1950—in response to a direct question I said: "I would say in the neighborhood of $600,000,000." But I added: "I would hate to be frozen to that, because you must appreciate that the estimates we are making today are on the cost of production units that have never been built before."

By April 1951, four months later, the very tentative total cost estimate of the Savannah River plant had climbed to $900,000,000, and by September of the same year to

$1,200,000,000. The September estimate was based on design work only ten-per-cent complete, although construction by then was well under way. Now it looks as if the plant in its final form will cost about $1,500,000,000.

This is not a pretty story, and I don't like it any better than the average taxpayer does. It can be said, of course, that much of the increased cost is due to improvements incorporated after construction began, to substantial increases in scope and size, and to such factors as the need to pay premium prices for many of the critical materials involved. But the fact remains that some bad estimates were made at the start. There was every reason why the estimates should not have been accurate, but they nevertheless were too unrealistic to be rationalized in this way.

I know, however, that the government is getting one dollar's worth of plant for every dollar invested in this project. It is not that money is being wasted here. Both the Commission and its contractor are seeing to that, and independent investigations sponsored by Congress have shown it to be true. It is, instead, that the final costs were not figured accurately enough in advance. But I don't think either the Commission or its contractor should be too severely censured for these poor cost guesses until all the returns are in. If this plant, when completed, fails to do any better than it was originally designed to do, then I think the Commission can be fairly criticized for a bad mistake in estimating. But if it does substantially better than it was at first designed to do—as I firmly believe it will, partly because of the costly improvements incorporated—then I would say our mistake was a relatively minor one compared with the end result, and can justifiably be forgiven.

A good many of the other perplexing difficulties stemming from the urgent need for speed in the Commission's construction program have to do with the problem of bringing vast quantities of men and materials together at

men already on the site as hard and as long as they were willing and able to work. This was done, and I believe he made the best possible decision under the circumstances. Everyone connected with the operation can take real pride in the fact that when H-hour of the first test day arrived the now-familiar blindingly bright light filled the desert sky, a roar reverberated through the Nevada hills, and a great mushroom-shaped cloud billowed miles up into the air. The deadline had been met, the test went off as planned, and the national security had been substantially advanced. But the overtime incident was a headache just the same, and the Commission immediately took steps to keep the need for such extensive overtime from arising again.

I have cited these few isolated, but more or less typical, examples of the headaches that go with a multibillion-dollar construction program as illustrations of the things that come along to harass the Commission as it tries to keep its mind and eyes focused on its main objective—optimum atomic strength in this country as soon as possible. They are the kinds of headaches that grow out of the dramatic and nasty incidents that require attention far out of proportion to their significance to the total program. You might think that barracks in South Carolina or plumbers in Nevada are rather far removed from the neutrons, reactors, and atomic bombs, but in actual practice they are not. They are a necessary part of the great effort being carried on to give substance and meaning in terms of national security to the ideas that generate in the minds of our scientists.

# CHAPTER vi

# The Payoff: Weapons

AT the end of the long, bustling atomic energy production line, with its far-flung exploration parties, remote mines, futuristic plants, and booming construction activity, lie the secret locations where our national stockpile of atomic weapons is stored. These weapons are the end product. They are what all the activity is about and what the production line is for. By merely reposing quietly in their hidden vaults they affect the lives of all of us and influence the course of world events.

There has probably been more talk about atomic weapons than about any other phase of atomic energy. Yet, there is probably less real understanding of what atomic weapons are, what they can do, and how they affect us, than there is about any other part of the atomic energy program. Too much of the talk is based on ignorance, too much of it is seasoned with speculation or sensationalism, and too much of it is garnished with fear or repulsion to make it very useful as a means of obtaining an objective understanding of what atomic weapons are really all about.

It is not surprising, in such a setting, to hear such contradictory comments as the following:

"The atom bomb is the most horrible and fiendish weapon ever devised by man. It's sinful for us to go on making them."

"The A-bomb doesn't amount to much; why, those soldiers out in Nevada were right up beside an explosion and weren't hurt at all. They were laughing when it was over."

"Did you see where the atomic energy people blew up a whole island in the Pacific? Why, they wiped it right off the map!"

"Atom bombs are bad all right, but if you live a couple of miles away from the nearest target, you'll be okay."

"If the Russians ever decide to let go on us with A-bombs, there won't be a thing we can do except clobber them back. Civil defense is just a waste of time—like throwing sand on a volcano."

"What I never could understand is why we didn't use a few A-bombs in Korea. We could have blasted those Reds right out of those hills and back to China."

"A-bombs are like poison gas; both sides have them and both sides are afraid to use them."

"The H-bomb? I want to keep my sanity; let's talk about baseball."

Much of the confusion is undoubtedly due to the reticence of the Atomic Energy Commission—a reticence calculated to deny useful knowledge to our potential enemies. Unfortunately, it also denies useful knowledge to our own people. But it is impossible to give information to the American public without also giving it to those who would use it against us. That is the dilemma, and it is generally solved by giving out certain basic information upon which reasonable and responsible people can reach valid conclusions, and withholding information that would help our possible enemies more than it would help us. This is often hard to do, but it is the objective.

I know there are those who say: "Fuchs and those fellows stole most of our old wartime secrets and gave them to the Russians; why not publish this information so our own people will know at least as much as the Russians?" This is good reasoning so far as it goes, except for one fatal fallacy: Spies, like the rest of us, are only human, and the information they pass on is subject to distortion and misinterpretation, just like the gossip at last night's bridge party or the report in yesterday's paper. It might just be that an official announcement over here could clear up the one point in a spy's report that had been left out or wrongly interpreted. But in any event, it is not so much the technical secrets on how to make weapons that help public understanding as it is information on what atomic bombs can do.

Part of the confusion about weapons, in my opinion, is due to those people outside of the program (some of them well-meaning) who have discovered that one can attract headline attention, and therefore a certain kind of fame, by saying things publicly about atomic bombs. It is a case of the self-styled expert rushing in where the government, for security reasons, fears to tread. Some of what these people say is true; a good deal of it is not. While this may be good for the national security, in that it may confuse our competitors, it is scarcely good for public understanding. And yet the government cannot censor the writings and utterances of these people in detail, for to do so would be to tell them exactly what the real secrets are and thus leave them free to pass the truth on to their friends or acquaintances, or perhaps even to publish it. Their demonstrated irresponsibility does not recommend them as good security risks. By the same token, the government also cannot publicly correct their misleading reports, for to do that would be to broadcast the secret we are trying to protect.

Sometimes I have heard it said that the government should censor these people just because what they say is misleading, or because they are talking in areas where they have "no business" to talk. As tempting as this solution is, it in many ways carries with it more dangers than the circulation of irresponsible reports, for governments that have engaged in this kind of activity have invariably found it hard to know where to stop. The "misleading" books found in Germany by Hitler's Nazi government made quite a bonfire.

Some of the misunderstanding about atomic weapons is probably also due to the small amount of experience the public has had with them. Fortunately, none has ever been exploded in the United States except under controlled test conditions. Of the at least forty-nine that have been detonated in various parts of the world, only six have been seen and studied by people not connected with the atomic energy programs or armed services of the United States, Great Britain, or the Soviet Union. Here is a chronology of the atomic explosions that have taken place throughout the world up to the time of this writing:

1945: Total of 3, all by the U.S., at Alamagordo, Hiroshima, and Nagasaki.

1946: Total of 2, both by the U.S., at Bikini Atoll in the Pacific.

1947: None.

1948: Total of 3, all by the U.S., at Eniwetok Atoll in the Pacific.

1949: Total of 1, by the U.S.S.R., "somewhere in the Soviet Union."

1950: None.

1951: Total of 18, including 12 by the U.S. in Nevada, 4 by the U.S. at Eniwetok, 2 by the U.S.S.R.

1952: Total of at least 11, including 8 by the U.S. in Nevada, at least 2 * by the U.S. at Eniwetok, 1 by the British at Monte Bello Island, Australia.

1953, up to July 1: Total of 11, all by the U.S. in Nevada.

* Exact number confidential at this writing.

Of all these, only the ones at Hiroshima and Nagasaki in 1945, the two at Bikini in 1946, and one each in the 1952 and 1953 series in Nevada have been seen relatively close up by unofficial observers. This is not, unfortunately, a very broad base upon which to build an accurate public understanding of atomic weapons and their capabilities. There will be more "open" shots, and there should be.

While the general paucity of official information on weapons has restricted public understanding to some degree, perhaps the most important obstacle results from the fact that atomic energy began as an entirely secret project which burst into world consciousness in the most spectacular and violent kind of way. Consequently, too many people still consider atomic weapons to be too secret to mention, or too horrible to contemplate; and they therefore close their minds to the authoritative facts the government has released to them. Too many others, apparently remembering Hiroshima, are inclined to believe every sensational report they hear, no matter what the source is, and the government's official remarks become lost in a general sea of rumor and speculation.

I think it is possible to bring some sense out of all this, and I shall attempt to do so later on in this chapter. But as part of the background, I believe it would be useful to look at some history.

To date, two atomic bombs, and only two, have been used as weapons of war. They were used not as so-called "tactical weapons" against troops in the field, but as "strategic weapons" delivered against the power of an embattled nation to continue to make war. They were used by the United States, and they were delivered by aircraft operating in skies over which we had won control and against an adversary who was not capable of retaliating either in kind or in any other effective way against our homeland.

As a result of the use of these bombs, two Japanese cities of moderate size were destroyed, with 100,000 fatali-

velopment of power-producing reactors. As we have seen, however, the Atomic Energy Commission is currently engaged in a huge expansion program, a fact which clearly suggests the stockpile is still not as large as we would like it to be. The government has made it plain that completion of these expanded facilities on a very high priority schedule will enable us to meet our minimum military stockpile requirements four years sooner than would otherwise be the case.

8. It has been announced that two tests in connection with the development of the H-bomb have been held, and that progress has been sufficient for the government to say that "we have entered another stage in the world-shaking development of atomic energy."

9. Soviet Russia, our hostile competitor, is also in the business of manufacturing atomic weapons, and has been since 1949. This does constitute a threat. Although we obviously hold a substantial lead over the Soviets, this is hardly an effective means of preventing them from accumulating enough bombs to deliver a knockout blow against us. It is true that the Russians have held but three tests at this writing, but this should not be a cause for complacency. Whereas such a small amount of test activity might well indicate a lack of variety, it can hardly be taken as an indication of a lack of quantity, for tests are a necessary part of developmental rather than production activity.

10. As the atomic stockpiles on both sides of the Iron Curtain continue to grow, leadership in the fields of atomic defense and delivery plays an increasingly important part in the world distribution of atomic power.

11. Taking world progress in atomic weapons manufacture and development into account, it is no longer realistic to think of such weapons as something so rare and expensive that they will necessarily have to be expended one at a time, or that their explosive power will

bear some fixed relationship to the bombs we have known in the past. Atomic weapons are absolute weapons, whether the target is a supply dump, a regiment, or a whole nation. The only realistic way to plan our defenses, therefore, including civil defense, is to assume that atomic weapons, if used against us at all, will be used in sufficient quantity and size to destroy thoroughly whatever target they are aimed at. The effects would probably be of the same type as those resulting from the blasts at Hiroshima and Nagasaki, but the degree might well be vastly different.

What does all this mean to you as an American citizen? What should be the program for survival for you and for our country in this age of atomic weapons? My proposal would include these points:

1. Whether you are a statesman or an ordinary citizen, you can work for and support the efforts being made to bring a real and stable peace to the world through the settlement of the differences now existing between nations and the reduction and international control of armaments.

2. In the absence of a real international settlement, you can support and work on behalf of this country's effort to reach as soon as possible its minimum military requirements for atomic weapons and the means of delivering them. The purpose of our weapons now, and their purpose in the future, is to deter war and aggression. If we can have on hand enough weapons to destroy an aggressor's industrial ability to make war, and to knock out his invading forces in the field, we will have done much to ease the threat of war by making aggression so unprofitable that no prudent government would attempt it. With a stockpile of weapons for strategic use we can deter a direct attack on our homeland, and with a stockpile of weapons for tactical use we can help deter such adventurous excursions as have taken place in recent years along the borders of the free and slave worlds.

3. You can work for and support the efforts being made to strengthen the air defense of our country, including such things as radar screens, interceptor aircraft, and missiles, and—of great importance—civilian ground observer stations. The more difficult we make it for an enemy to get through to his target with enough bombs to make the attack worth while, the larger will be the force he must launch, and the smaller will be the chance he will launch it.

4. You can work for and support the efforts being made to give this country a strong civil-defense program. A good civil-defense program means fewer casualties, perhaps fifty per cent fewer, and less property damage in case of attack. The more damage and casualties are minimized, the harder it becomes for the enemy to launch a knock-out blow, and the smaller is the chance he will attempt to launch it. A good civil-defense program is a vital part of our national strategic planning, even if it never has to be used in an emergency. By participating in your local civil-defense activity, you may not only be increasing the chances of yourself and your loved ones to survive in case of an attack, you may also be helping to prevent the attack from occurring in the first place. Rest assured, your efforts are being considered in the calculations of those who would do us harm. The hunter does not want merely to wound the lion; for his own safety's sake he wants to kill it with one blow. So it would be in an all-out atomic war; our adversary will want to kill us, not merely wound us, and the harder you make it for him to accomplish this, the smaller is the chance he will attack at all.

There is a sign I have seen along many highways in our country. It reads: "Drive carefully; the life you save may be your own." This is good advice, and we might all take it—ourselves, our allies, and our potential enemies—and apply it to the atomic age: "Think carefully, act wisely; the life you save may be your own."

# CHAPTER *vii*

## *The Military and the Atom*

THE ATOMIC ENERGY COMMISSION is a civilian organization. The law creating it was written that way, and I, for one, hope that, in this respect at least, it will never be rewritten. If, however, the military establishment is to be trained in the use of atomic weapons, and if we are to achieve atomic readiness, there must be the closest possible relationship between the military and the Commission. In this chapter I will indicate how this relationship is achieved, and how it might be improved in some respects. To do this is to raise questions that go beyond the military's role in the atomic energy program and touch upon our total national security.

Top Russian military strategists cannot help but have a fairly accurate notion of our atomic weapon strength. In my opinion this has been sufficient to deter them from any full-scale aggressions which they may have planned for the continents of Europe and Asia. It follows that if we would continue to deter them we must remain strong. It does not follow, however, that we need match them twenty to one, or ten to one, or even one to one, in atomic bombs forever—certainly not if deterrence is our primary objective, as indeed it should be. Simply staying "ahead"

But the testing of weapons is an example of technical and administrative co-operation. The main problem, and one with which every American should be concerned, is the lack of real co-operation—under the present system—between the military and civilian authorities of the government in the development of national defense policy. What is needed is a basic rearrangement of the lines of command, the assignment of responsibility, and the mechanics of liaison. Atomic energy is but one example of the inadequacy of the present arrangement. There are others, and they are just as vitally connected with the general welfare of the nation. If we are to continue to survive the strains and stresses of the cold war and the preparedness program, these fundamental faults in the present system must be corrected all along the line.

# CHAPTER viii

# Power: The Peaceful Goal—
## First Phase

PROBABLY the most widely discussed subject in atomic energy, after "the bomb," is something we have come to call "atomic power." There is ample reason why this should be true, for of all the potential peaceful uses of the atom, the production of useful power is the one with the brightest promise of early, large-scale realization. It is important, therefore, that we understand exactly what we are talking about when we use the phrase "atomic power."

Although the terminology that has grown up in the still new field of atomic energy is subject to varying interpretations, the words "atomic power," when used in connection with the peaceful utilization of the atom, generally mean but one thing: heat. Most of the energy released in a controlled nuclear chain reaction appears in the form of heat, just as the energy in, say, a coal fire, which is a chemical chain reaction, also appears in this form. In other words, the phrase "atomic power" is used in much the same way as "coal power" or "oil power"; that is, the atom is the fuel and not something that is sent out over a transmission line. Atomic power is not, therefore, like electricity, although it can, like coal power, be used to produce electricity, just

Gaseous-Diffusion Plant K-25, at Oak Ridge, with Auxiliary Process Plant K-27 in foreground. Built during World War II, K-25 is the largest continuous process plant in the world under one roof. (*Courtesy of Westcott, Oak Ridge, Tenn.*)

The Oak Ridge Pile, which produces most of the radioisotopes used in this country. The substances to be irradiated are pushed in with a long rod through a carrier aligned with an opening in the pile. (*Courtesy Albert Fenn, Life Magazine.*)

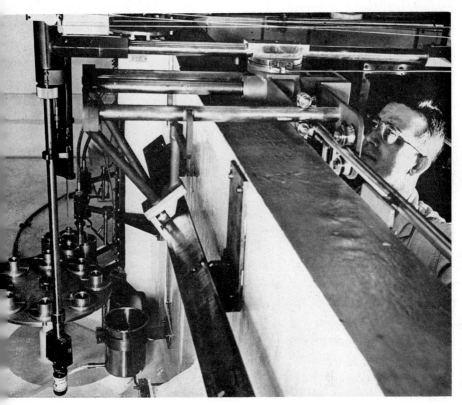

adioisotope shipping bottle being handled mechanically by remote
trol at Oak Ridge. (*Courtesy Oak Ridge National Laboratory.*)

Part of the "downtown" section of Oak Ridge. (*U. S. Army Photograph.*)

The west face of the Brookhaven reactor, showing physicists and chemists on the first balcony measuring the energy of neutrons emerging from the reactor. On the ground floor and upper balcony, health physicists with monitoring equipment for detecting radiation leakage. (*Courtesy Brookhaven National Laboratory.*)

The Brookhaven cosmotron. (*Courtesy Brookhaven National Laboratory.*)

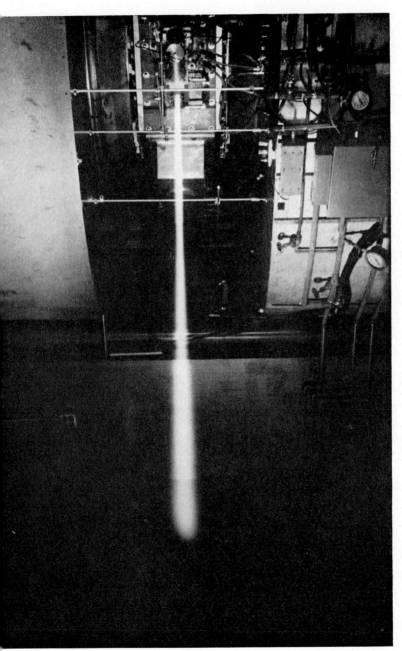

A beam of deuterons emerging from the acceleration chamber of the cyclotron at Argonne National Laboratory. (*Courtesy Argonne National Laboratory.*)

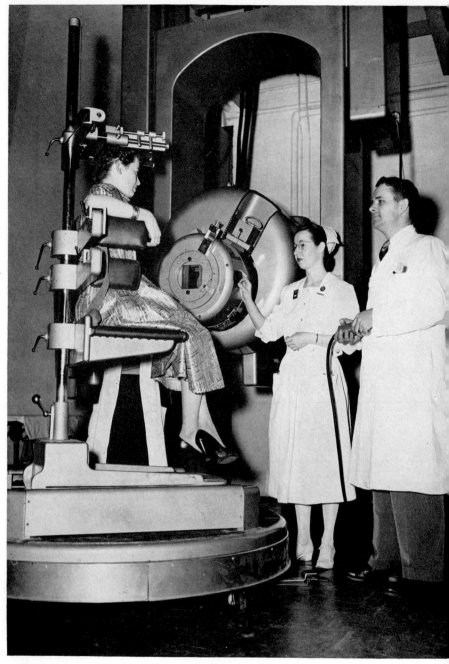

Demonstration of the use of a Van de Graaff generator in the treatment of cancer at Argonne Cancer Research Hospital. The patient is rotated under the X-ray beam. (*Courtesy Argonne National Laboratory.*)

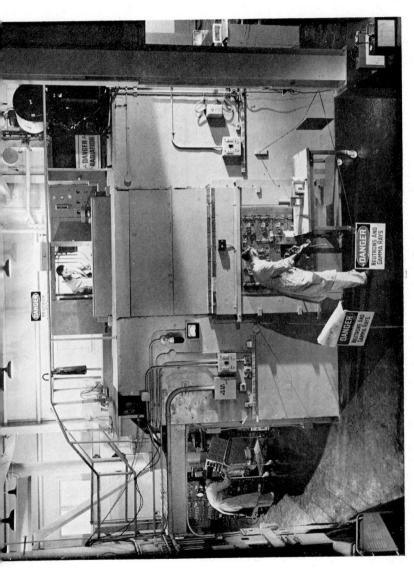

The Water Boiler Reactor at Los Alamos.
(*Courtesy United States Atomic Energy Commission.*)

A section of the Los Alamos residential area. (*Courtesy United States Atomic Energy Commission.*)

The 184-inch cyclotron at the University of California in Berkeley.
(Courtesy University of California, Berkeley, California.)

One of the main plutonium plants in the Hanford area at Richland.
(*Courtesy Johnson, Richland, Washington.*)

The Materials Testing Reactor shown here is but one of the facilities on the 400,000-acre National Reactor Testing Station in Idaho. The reactors are widely separated in the interest of safety. (*Courtesy United States Atomic Energy Commission.*)

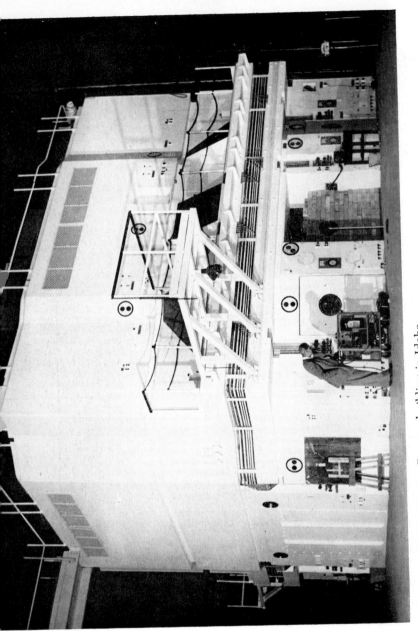

Inside the Materials Testing Reactor building in Idaho.
(*Courtesy United States Atomic Energy Commission.*)

The Experimental Breeder Reactor at the National Reactor Testing Station in Idaho. It produced power in 1951, and in 1952 demonstrated the feasibility of "breeding." (*Courtesy United States Atomic Energy Commission.*)

How a Nevada weapons test looks to the official observers seven miles away.
This is the explosion of an atomic artillery shell. Spring test, 1953.

as it can be used to do most of the other things that large quantities of heat can do.

In a sense, it would be entirely correct to describe a controlled nuclear chain reaction as a nuclear "fire" in which atomic "fuels" (called fissionable materials) are "burned" (fissioned) to produce heat for useful purposes. As in the case of a chemical fire, "ashes" (called fission products) are left over after the nuclear fire has been extinguished.

Although a nuclear fire resembles a chemical fire in that heat is produced and ashes remain, that is about the end of the similarity. Furthermore, there are a number of striking differences:

1. The quantity of heat produced per unit weight of fuel is vastly greater in a nuclear fire than in a chemical fire. For example, one pound of the atomic fuel, uranium-235, if burned in a nuclear way, will release 2,600,000 times the amount of heat produced from burning a pound of coal. This, of course, is the great appeal of atomic power, and the one single fact that makes the whole difficult game worth the candle.

2. Whereas, for all practical purposes, a chemical fire can exist only in an atmosphere in which oxygen is present, a nuclear fire can exist only in an atmosphere made up of billions upon billions of the incredibly small, invisible atomic fragments called neutrons. A nuclear fire, therefore, "feeds" on neutrons. But neutrons not only cause atoms to fission; they themselves are produced by the fission process. Thus a nuclear fire itself creates the means by which it is propagated. The fire is controlled, therefore, by controlling the number of neutrons it has access to, much as one can control a coal fire by governing the amount of air available to it. Neutrons are so important to atomic energy that some people call the program "the neutron business."

3. Whereas there are many materials on earth (coal,

wood, petroleum) that can be made to burn in a chemical way, there is only one naturally occurring substance that can be made to burn in a nuclear way. This is the very rare variety of uranium known as "235," which constitutes but seven tenths of one per cent of the metal uranium as it is found in nature. Fortunately for the future of atomic power, there are two other naturally occurring substances that can be made into atomic fuels: uranium-238 and thorium, which can be changed into "inflammable" plutonium and uranium-233, respectively. This can be done, interestingly enough, by exposing them over a period of time to a dense atmosphere of neutrons, such as that created by a nuclear chain reaction in uranium-235. Thus, a nuclear fire not only produces the means by which it is propagated; it also produces the means by which additional supplies of atomic fuel can be produced. Uranium-238 and thorium are more than a hundred times as plentiful in nature as uranium-235, and together with "235" they constitute the fuels of the atomic age.

4. A nuclear fire, unlike a chemical fire, is invisible. In burning, it creates large amounts of invisible nuclear radiations, similar to X rays, which are dangerous to humans and damaging to certain types of materials. For this reason, as we have seen, a nuclear fire must be surrounded by a thick shield of lead or concrete or water to seal in this dangerous radioactivity. In addition, the ashes left over from a nuclear fire remain "hot" in a radioactive sense for very long periods of time and must therefore be handled with the utmost care.

5. Unlike a chemical fire, a nuclear fire cannot be ignited until a certain minimum amount of fuel, called a "critical mass," has been assembled. Below this amount, not enough neutrons are produced by fissioning atoms to make the fuel burn. Above this amount, however, the fuel reacts spontaneously.

It will be recalled from Chapter III that the devices in

some cases it amounted to no more than one tenth of a watt. But not one of them produced anything that by the wildest stretch of the imagination could be called usable power.

Then, in 1951 and 1953, there came two reactors, the EBR in Idaho and the HRE at Oak Ridge, that actually produced some usable power in experimental quantities. And now, except for the bomb-material reactors at the Savannah River plant, the Commission's reactor development program is mainly pointed in the direction of developing reactors to produce power for a practical military purpose: propulsion of submarines, aircraft, and ships. We have progressed, therefore, from the purely research phase, through the usable-power-for-experimental-purposes phase, to the usable-power-for-practical-purposes phase. But we have yet to enter the phase where atomic power becomes economically feasible; that is, where the atom produces usable power for a practical purpose at a price that can compete with power from coal, oil, or gas.

There is likely to be some difficulty, as a matter of fact, in recognizing when economically feasible atomic power is actually here. Obviously what is economically feasible or competitive in one part of the world is not necessarily competitive in another. In some regions, such as the remote areas of Africa, the South Pacific, or the Arctic, electric power may cost as much as three cents per kilowatt hour to produce. In certain other places, even in our own western United States, power may cost from ten mills to two cents per kilowatt hour to produce. Even in a city such as Chicago production costs may amount to six or seven mills per kilowatt hour, and yet in other places, such as the Pacific Northwest, where falling water is plentiful, be as low as 2.5 mills.

What, then, is really meant by the phrase "economically feasible power"? If we were to take the Arctic as an example, it might mean something that was terrifically expensive by New York or Pittsburgh standards, and yet, for the Arctic, much cheaper than the cost of hauling in heavy shipments of coal or oil to fuel an orthodox power plant. In short, therefore, when we speak of economic feasibility, we are speaking of relative, and not absolute, costs, a fact which suggests that the first reactor to produce usable power for a practical civilian purpose should be located in an area where normal fuel costs are high. There are some, in fact, who say that there are places in the world, and even this country, where it would be feasible to do this now, today.

This might be true, but there are several drawbacks to such an approach in the year 1953. Inasmuch as a stationary reactor designed solely to produce power for a practical purpose has never been built, the scientists are not at all sure of the best design or the most economical size. A small reactor producing 10,000 kilowatts of electric energy might be built today for $10,000,000 and produce electricity at fifty mills per kilowatt hour. But a reactor costing only six times as much might be expected to produce twenty-five times as much electric energy at eight mills per kilowatt hour.

No one, of course, knows any of these things for certain, for the simple reason that no real atomic power plant has yet been built and operated. Many of our cost calculations will depend to a large extent upon what we learn in the immediate future about the construction of power reactors. But units of the size described, and at the cost indicated, appear to be feasible and will probably produce power at approximately the prices quoted.

# CHAPTER ix

## Power: The Peaceful Goal— Second Phase

W E are today in the beginnings of a period of intensive and exciting development work in the field of power reactors, but it is questionable whether the best results can be achieved if the first power reactors are put down in isolated, high-cost areas remote from existing laboratories and scientists. The first reactor designed specifically for civilian power purposes would very logically be a pilot, rather than a full-scale, plant. And if it is to play the most useful role possible as a pilot plant, its location should be governed not by the cost of competitive fuels but by the availability of existing talent in the reactor field—that is, the men who will design it, build it, operate it, and learn from it. And if this is true, it will have to be primarily a developmental rather than a commercial device.

Since reactors are still in the developmental stage, they are not only more expensive than they will be later on, but are also less efficient and less reliable. You can use a costly and inefficient plant in a submarine, where the expense is outweighed by the military advantage you gain (the STR prototype in Idaho cost $20,000,000, exclusive of fuel—an expensive engine for a submarine), but the operator of an electric generating plant or a commercial freighter wants the most inexpensive, efficient, and reliable source of heat he can find.

A commercial power plant, to be economically feasible, must not only cost a reasonable figure to build; it must also operate at very high temperature levels for very long periods of time without costly repairs, shutdowns, or replacements, and it must convert large quantities of heat efficiently into usable power.

The problem of gaining very high temperatures and holding them for long periods of time is a particularly bothersome and expensive one. It mainly involves finding and producing quantities of materials that can withstand both high temperatures and extremely high levels of nuclear radiation. As an added difficulty, the materials must not absorb the neutrons that feed the reaction. Unfortunately, there are not many materials that meet these rigid specifications, and to find and produce them in quantity requires a good deal of time and money. For one thing, the search for new materials required construction of the $18,000,000 Materials Testing Reactor in Idaho. Another example of the cost involved in this materials problem is the metal zirconium. Zirconium, which was first produced in pure form by the atomic energy project from the same material as the soft, diamondlike stone, the zircon, is an excellent reactor construction material, meeting all the rigid specifications. But the first zirconium produced cost $300 a pound—dollars that in all fairness should be charged up to the first reactor using the material. Zirconium now costs but $15 per pound and the price is still falling—a good example of why the price of a reactor may be expected to drop substantially as the technology advances.

The problem of extracting usable power efficiently from the heat produced in a reactor is also a difficult and challenging one, involving airtight, corrosion-resistant, radia-

a new source of electricity that probably will take only a few pennies a month, if that, off their monthly light bill.

This is, however, the case, and here is why: To produce electricity an atomic power plant needs all of the electrical generating and distribution equipment that a coal-burning plant needs. The only difference is that in the atomic plant the coal hopper and steam boiler would be replaced by a nuclear reactor and a different kind of steam boiler. There is no chance, therefore, of reducing the cost of the plant by going to the atom for fuel. As a matter of fact, it seems quite possible that atomic power plants will always cost more to build than coal plants—they certainly do now—because a nuclear reactor is, by its very nature, vastly more expensive than a coal furnace.

The place, then, where you can save money by going over to atomic power is in the cost of the fuel. And here you do save money, because the atom packs so much energy into such a small space. This means that your fuel, per unit of heat, not only comes more cheaply in the first place; it also means that you save money all along the line on transportation, handling, and storage charges. So great is this saving that some economists, when calculating the cost of atomic power, put the cost of the nuclear fuel down as virtually zero. But it is important to remember that, even if coal were mined and distributed free to electric generating plants today, the reduction in your monthly electricity bill would amount to but twenty per cent, so great is the cost of the plant itself and the distribution system.

To express it in the simplest terms: You can save a lot of money on fuel if you have an atomic power plant, but it will cost a great deal more to build than a coal-burning plant. Since atomic fuel is so cheap, you can, of course, afford to pay more for your atomic plant, but somewhere there is a ceiling below which you must stay. Dr. W. H.

Zinn of the Commission's Argonne Laboratory, one of the country's leading reactor scientists, has figured that one may spend no more than $60,000,000 for an atomic power plant designed to produce as much electricity (200,000 kilowatts) as a coal-burning plant costing $40,000,000. This is, of course, a permissible fifty-per-cent increase in cost over conventional facilities, and it is, essentially, the cost figure that the scientists and technicians must shoot at to make economically feasible atomic power.

But even if the ultimate cost of atomic power comes out at about the same or slightly less than the cost of power from conventional sources today, it is still well worth the effort to achieve it. I say this for several reasons.

First, the energy the world uses today comes from coal, oil, gas, wood, or falling water. Of these, all but wood and falling water, which together can supply only a fraction of the world's energy needs, are exhaustible. They are being used up and they cannot be replaced. Ultimately, therefore, we are going to run out of coal, oil, and gas, and meanwhile, as we work through the more accessible deposits, the cost of these fuels will steadily rise. The world, therefore, is in need of a new source of energy. This source is more badly needed in some countries, such as Great Britain, France, Belgium, Italy, and Sweden, where coal and oil reserves are short or nonexistent, than it is in the United States, where coal and oil are still relatively plentiful and cheap. But the world as a whole, including the United States, needs a new source of energy, and it will need it increasingly as each year passes.

In this situation, it is interesting to consider some facts turned up by Palmer C. Putnam, a consulting engineer who recently conducted a survey on world energy sources for the Atomic Energy Commission. Mr. Putnam, for purposes of simplicity, uses an energy unit known as a "Q," which is equal to a billion billion British Thermal Units of heat. Using this unit, it can be shown that the world is presently consuming energy at a rate of 20 Q per century, and that, if present trends continue, this rate will have climbed to 100 Q per century by the year 2000. This calculation includes energy consumption in all forms: for propelling ships, automobiles, trains, and aircraft; for heating homes, offices, and factories; for supplying heat for industrial processes; and for producing electric power.

It is sobering to match these figures against the best estimates of the world's reserves of coal, oil, and gas. For economically recoverable coal, the reserve estimate is about 70 Q, and for oil and gas together it is about 8 Q. If these estimates are correct, and they are probably not too far wrong, the world's fuel reserves would last for about 400 years at the present rate of consumption, and for less than 80 years at the rate of consumption that will very likely be reached by the year 2000. Whatever the margin of error here, it is plain, I think, that we cannot continue to rely forever upon our traditional sources of energy.

Under these circumstances, it is encouraging to note that if all the economically recoverable uranium and thorium in the world could be converted into energy, it would provide a new source of energy amounting to about 1,700 Q, or enough for seventeen centuries even at the rate of consumption that we may expect to reach by the year 2000. When contrasted with the 70 Q in the world's coal reserves, this is an impressive figure.

These facts alone are sufficient justification for trying very hard to slip a harness on the atom. Moreover, I think it would be foodhardy to wait until every other kind of fuel runs out before we try to harness the atom, for there will always be special purposes for which coal, oil, and gas will be useful even in an atomic age. The sooner we can take even part of the total power burden off these conventional fuels, the longer they will last to serve the purposes for which they are uniquely suited. An electric power industry based on atomic energy would be a tremendous boon in itself, for, just in this one place, about twenty per cent of our annual consumption of coal, gas, and oil could be made available for other purposes or saved for future specialized use. Another place where the atom would be of immediate benefit would be in the propulsion of ships. If our entire Navy and merchant marine were converted to atomic energy, a substantial percentage of our oil reserves could be immediately conserved for later use for such purposes as automobile propulsion—a function to which a nuclear reactor, with all its bulky shielding, may never be suited.

In all of these energy calculations there has until recently been one highly important "if." Thus, we could expect to find these great quantities of energy in the atom only *if* we could convert all of the economically minable uranium in the world into fissionable material. And we could stretch these even further only *if* we could also convert all of the economically minable thorium in the world into fissionable material. In this connection, I had the great pleasure of making the following announcement shortly before I completed my term as Chairman of the Atomic Energy Commission:

"We have now reached still another milestone in the history of atomic energy development in this country. It is a development which holds out the promise of making a civilian atomic power industry even more feasible and attractive in the long range than it has hitherto appeared to be.

"To explain to you the impact of reaching this new milestone, I would like to use an analogy, albeit a greatly oversimplified one. I would like to ask you to imagine a world in which only one hundred gallons of gasoline existed. When that gasoline was used up, gasoline would forever be gone from the earth. But let us imagine that we could make gasoline out of water by burning the gasoline we had in the presence of water. Let us say, for ex-

tion of electric energy and the production of heat to propel various means of transportation. What is beyond these no one today knows. At the time when Morse sent his famous "What hath God wrought?" message over the first wireless, how many people could visualize the progress in the field of electronics that has led to radar and television? Even if we had no other reason to apply ourselves diligently in the field of atomic power, our current ignorance of the art and the obscure but tantalizingly promising future should be enough in itself to beckon us on.

# CHAPTER X

## Radioisotopes: Servants of Man

I REMEMBER a press conference which took place at Atomic Energy Commission headquarters in Washington shortly after I became a Commissioner. The purpose of the conference was to familiarize the members of the press with the many beneficial things that were being accomplished throughout the world by the use of those valuable by-products of the atomic energy program called "radioisotopes." As a Commissioner, I was expected to be on hand for the conference, but as a new Commissioner I was not expected to say much. Present to answer the technical questions of the press were several scientists from the Commission's staff. This was an excellent arrangement from my point of view, for I was not yet very familiar with the isotope part of the atomic energy program, and I welcomed the opportunity to listen and learn.

I well remember the first question from the floor: "Just what," asked one gentleman of the press, "is an isotope?" There followed a rather lengthy discussion about atomic weights and masses, mixed in with numerous references to neutrons and protons, the composition of atomic nuclei, and the periodic table of the elements. A blackboard was brought out and several diagrams were drawn upon it with a good many white and black circles representing the constituent parts of an atom. During the prolonged discussion many of the more erudite members of the press asked questions which were answered in considerable detail.

Finally the questioning stopped, and the scientists who had undertaken to cover this particular subject prepared to move on to another. But before doing so they invited a last question or two from anyone wishing to clear up a point that might not yet be fully understood. In response, the man who had asked the original question raised his hand, very thoughtfully leaned forward, and said: "There is one small point I am not yet completely clear on. What exactly," he inquired, "is an isotope?"

It is this inability of most people to understand what an isotope is that has, in my view, prevented isotopes from receiving the credit they deserve for the contribution to human betterment they have already made in this very early stage of atomic energy development. Actually isotopes constitute perhaps the happiest chapter in the story of the atom. They are used to treat the sick, to learn more about disease, to improve manufacturing processes, to increase the productivity of crops and livestock, and to help man to understand the basic processes of his body, the living things around him, and the physical world in which he exists. Here, in the field of isotopes, there are no difficult questions of policy to thrash out, and very few questions of law or economics to decide. And there is no question of waiting for benefits to materialize in the future. They are here now—at least some of them—and they are already beginning to change and improve our lives in many more ways than most people realize.

But just what is an isotope? I am not sure I can succeed in making this clear where others have failed. Perhaps the best definition I have ever heard is this: "An isotope is something that is exactly like something else only it is different." At first glance, this does not appear to shed much light on the question of what an isotope is. But perhaps it can be made to if we look briefly at a little history.

When man began his life on earth he found things around him which he could identify. He identified the air he breathed, the water he drank, the plants and animals he ate, the wool and coal he burned, the stone and earth from which he built his shelter, and the salt with which he seasoned his food. As time passed he learned that most of these things were made up of other, more basic substances. Thus he found that water was really made up of the gases oxygen and hydrogen and that salt was made up of sodium and chlorine combined in a way that completely changed the characteristics and properties of the original substances. Ultimately he discovered that there were only ninety-two substances that occurred naturally on earth and that were not combinations of something else. They were "pure." All other things, he learned, were really combinations of two or more of these basic building blocks which, because of their elemental nature, he called "elements." Among the ninety-two basic elements he identified such very light substances as hydrogen, carbon, and oxygen, such heavier substances as silver, iron, and zinc, and such very heavy substances as gold, uranium, and lead.

For a very long time man thought that all of the material which went to make up any one of these ninety-two basic elements was exactly alike. Thus, he thought that all hydrogen was identical with all other hydrogen, and that all uranium was identical with all other uranium. There was a very good reason why he should believe this, for all hydrogen looked and acted like all other hydrogen and all uranium looked and acted like all other uranium. In fact, this appeared to be true of every one of the ninety-two basic elements he could separate and identify.

But now, man realizes that in some cases there are dif-

tain tremendous amounts of radioactivity, which might be used by industry in various ways.

Possible uses of fission products have been studied by the Stanford Research Institute under contract with the Atomic Energy Commission. A report issued by this organization in 1951 indicated that a potential large-scale industrial demand exists for fission products, but that the magnitude of the demand will depend greatly upon price. If fission products can be sold very cheaply, large quantities might be used by industry.

Before fission products can be made available to industry on a large scale, however, both technical problems (such as the design of separation plants) and marketing problems (such as pricing, patent, and safety policies) will have to be solved. Separation processes are particularly costly today, and a good deal of research may have to be done before fission products become an economically feasible proposition. In addition, industry will have to know considerably more about their utilization than is known today. Several fission-product sources of high-intensity radiation are being used in research in this field.

If fission products can be made available to industry at $100 per curie (a "curie" is equivalent to $20,000 worth of radium) or less, the Stanford Research Institute has reported, they could be used for static eliminators, for making permanently fluorescent light tubes, and for manufacturing new types of chemicals. If the price were brought down to $5 per curie, their use in industrial radiography would be practical. At $2 per curie they could be used for sterilizing various drugs, such as penicillin, without the use of heat. Below $1 per curie, the Institute has concluded, they might be used for the sterilization of various foods.

This last use is problematical at our present stage of knowledge. Destruction of all micro-organisms in food requires a very high dose of radiation, and the amount necessary may affect the taste or even produce toxic substances. Sterilization of drugs is a more promising possibility, at least in the immediate future.

In this chapter I have tried to review some of the ways in which radioisotopes now are being used in biology, medicine, agriculture, chemistry, and in various industries. No one can predict today all the other uses which may be developed. Future applications of radioisotopes, particularly in research, are limited only by the ingenuity of the men who use them. But it is safe to say that they will continue to be powerful and versatile research tools as long as man seeks to increase his understanding of the processes of life and the nature of the world around him.

# CHAPTER *xi*

## *The Quest for Knowledge*

IF you have ever looked through a powerful telescope at
the night sky, or visited a planetarium, you probably have
at least a faint idea of the kinds of worlds that exist beyond the range of human experience and understanding.

One such world is the world of the atom. Unlike the
Milky Way or the Spiral Nebula, however, no one has
ever seen an atom, even in broad outline. Atoms are far
too tiny. They are as infinitely small as the universe is
infinitely large. Even the most powerful microscope fails
by many thousands of times to bring the bulkiest atoms
into view. And yet, by developing many theories, by testing them over many years of painstaking experimentation,
and then by revising and adjusting them until they explain at least in part the things that happen in the world
that man understands and knows, man has succeeded in
learning a good deal about atoms and what they can be
made to do.

Surprisingly enough—or perhaps unsurprisingly—the
world of the atom, as currently visualized by man, is not
too different from that of the stars. If you could reduce
yourself in size until you were even smaller in relation to
an atom than you now are in relation to the earth, you
could enter this world. What you would find there no one

really knows, but you would probably find something that was not vastly different from what you might encounter if you were traveling in a space ship deep in the Milky Way. Most of the space around you would be completely empty, and yet, at intervals, for as far as your eyes could see, there would be "suns" and "stars" and "planets." There would even be "comets" and "meteors" and, here and there, an exploding star or one that was, by violent eruption, disgorging fragments of itself out into atomic space.

Such, according to what we know today, is the world of the atom. It is an orderly world, and yet, so far as man is concerned, it is a complicated and still largely mysterious one. Man has learned a lot about this world, but, as with the universe itself, the more he learns the more there seems to be to learn. The really fundamental truths always seem to lie just beyond the reach of the most brilliant human minds and the most intricate man-made equipment. But in spite of these many drawbacks, man today knows, or thinks he knows, enough about atoms to be able to construct, in general terms, a fairly clear if symbolic picture of one.

According to current theory, an individual atom is similar, roughly, to the solar system of which our earth is a part. It has a dense, inner core, called a "nucleus," corresponding to the sun, and one or more incredibly small surrounding particles called "electrons," corresponding to the planets. If you could enlarge an average-sized atom until its nucleus was as big as a basketball, its electron planets would be about a mile away. So small is the nucleus, however, that if you took a bowl of water and increased it in size until it was as big as the earth, you would still need a microscope to distinguish the individual nuclei and electrons within it.

Man has known for a long time that the nucleus of an

atom and the electrons which surround it are both electrically charged, with the nucleus bearing a positive charge and the electrons a negative one. He has also known for many years that the electrons in an atom are but loosely bound to their nuclear "sun" by this electric attraction, and that it is interactions between the electrons of different atoms that build the molecules of the substances which make up the world as you and I know it. These electronic interactions, for example, account for the way in which atoms of oxygen and hydrogen can be bound together to form water. They also account for such ordinary chemical reactions as the burning of coal, the manufacture of drugs and chemicals, and the explosion of dynamite. But the hearts of atoms—their nuclei—are undisturbed by these sometimes violent goings-on along the outer edges of their atomic domains. They can even preserve their nuclear equanimity through the explosion of a TNT blockbuster bomb.

It is with these atomic nuclei that the science of atomic energy deals. The purpose of the atomic energy program is to learn as much about these hearts of atoms as possible, and then to put that knowledge to work. As yet, scientists do not know very much about atomic nuclei, but what little they do know has made possible the atomic bomb, nuclear reactors, and radioisotopes. What additional wonders may be hidden in the tiny hearts of atoms no one today can even guess.

Most scientists now agree that the basic building blocks of an atomic nucleus are the particles of matter called protons and neutrons. Both are about two thousand times heavier than an electron, but are still incredibly small. They differ in that the proton bears a positive charge and the neutron has no charge at all. It is the protons in a nucleus that give it its positive charge and cause it to attract and hold in their orbits the electron planets which go to make up the outer portions of an atom. In a normal atom there is always one electron planet for each proton in the nucleus.

Both of these particles are enormously important. The number of protons in a nucleus, for example, determines the kind of chemical substance the atom is. The number of neutrons, together with the number of protons, determines the weight of the atom and therefore the isotope it is. Neutrons also determine the atom's stability. Thus, if there are too many or too few neutrons in relation to the number of protons present, the nucleus may spontaneously throw out a small charged particle or two as it adjusts itself to a more stable combination. Atoms which do this are said to be radioactive, and each time they emit a particle they change into an entirely different kind of material. Radium, the most plentiful radioactive element in nature, will do this a number of times at highly irregular intervals over the course of many thousands of years, ultimately becoming lead, which is stable.

The simplest atom in existence is that of ordinary hydrogen gas—the lightest element on earth—which consists of but one proton as the nucleus and one electron planet. It is the only atom which has no neutrons at all in its nucleus. If you were to take an ordinary hydrogen nucleus and add a neutron to it, you would have a substance known as "heavy hydrogen," or deuterium, which is the ingredient in heavy water that makes it heavier than normal water. Heavy hydrogen, although it weighs more than ordinary hydrogen, is still hydrogen, however, because it still has but one proton in its nucleus. If you were to add another proton to heavy hydrogen you would have a rare kind of helium.

The biggest and most complicated atom in nature is that of ordinary uranium metal, which contains 92 protons and 146 electrons bound tightly together in the nucleus. This metal, because it contains 238 particles in its

be put to work is in the production of power, discussed in Chapters VIII and IX. One of the main centers of this kind of research is the Argonne National Laboratory at Lemont, Illinois, on the outskirts of Chicago. Argonne is the successor to the famed Metallurgical Project of World War II which built the first nuclear chain reactor. The laboratory is operated for the Commission by the University of Chicago and is under the direction of one of the world's foremost reactor scientists, Dr. Walter H. Zinn. Thirty-two educational institutions and research laboratories in twelve midwestern states are affiliated with Argonne and maintain research and training programs in co-operation with it.

The Argonne Laboratory occupies a newly built home which replaces the makeshift facilities used by the Metallurgical Project during the war. These were located in a score or so of temporary locations scattered in and around Chicago. The laboratory today, which occupies a rural site about twenty-five miles west of downtown Chicago, looks much like many well-kept industrial laboratories, with its low-lying red brick buildings and wide lawns. None of the laboratory's staff of about 2,000 lives on the fenced-in site. Many of them live in the quiet village of Lemont, while many others commute daily from Chicago and its suburbs.

In the years since the war, Argonne has maintained its pre-eminence in the reactor field. Among other things, it designed and operates the Experimental Breeder Reactor which first produced usable electrical power and which first demonstrated the feasibility of breeding. It also performed the basic design and development work on the first atomic power plant for submarine propulsion, and assisted with the design of the production reactors at the Savannah River plant in South Carolina.

Another important center of reactor research and development work is the Oak Ridge National Laboratory at Oak Ridge, Tennessee. It is operated for the Commission by the Union Carbide and Carbon Corporation, as are the gaseous-diffusion plants located on the Oak Ridge reservation. Like Los Alamos, the Oak Ridge Laboratory has its own town, where most of its 3,000 employees live.

The Oak Ridge National Laboratory is located in a valley away from the town. Its main building is large, new, and severely functional. This would be the administrative center of the Oak Ridge Laboratory and also the home of much of its technical equipment. Surrounding this new headquarters are a number of smaller, shedlike structures containing, among other facilities, experimental models of new types of reactors, such as the Homogeneous Reactor Experiment discussed in Chapter VIII. Oak Ridge is also a center of research work leading to the development of an atomic engine for aircraft.

The largest building on the laboratory grounds outside of the headquarters houses the world-famed Oak Ridge reactor, producer of most of the radioisotopes that are shipped by the Atomic Energy Commission to all corners of the United States and the free world. Near the reactor itself is the distribution center for the radioisotope program, where the isotopes are separated, packaged, and shipped.

In addition to its many research, development, and production activities, Oak Ridge also is a major training center in the atomic energy field. It is, for example, the home of the Atomic Energy Commission's Reactor Training School. It is also the headquarters of the Oak Ridge Institute of Nuclear Studies, an organization of thirty leading universities in fourteen southern states, the District of Columbia, and Puerto Rico. The Institute operates several fellowship programs in atomic energy, arranges for faculty members of its associated institutions to perform research work with the Oak Ridge Laboratory's specialized equipment, and carries out the Atomic Energy Comso, nothing in his deportment, short of his actual physical contacts with Russian agents—which could have been discovered only by constant shadowing of him—would have raised the slightest suspicion.

Klaus Fuchs was a serious-minded bachelor, detached, retiring, shy, displaying little humor. While at Los Alamos he was much sought after as a baby sitter. He was unusually competent in his field, a distinguished theoretical physicist who talked little of politics and world problems. He was neither very much liked nor disliked, and he was actually not very well known to his colleagues.

Klaus Fuchs was a perfectionist, contemptuous of those who were not. Interestingly enough, he was outwardly conscientious when it came to security matters, and in declassification conferences he took a fairly conservative attitude toward the release of technical information to the public. He was meticulous in the handling of secret documents and in maintaining high security standards in his own office. He had a methodical brain, and he possessed a high degree of self-composure. Superficially he appeared to be one who abided by all of the rules of the game—the rules of the laboratory, the rules of the office—but basically he was beholden only to his own conscience.

But how was anyone to know what that conscience dictated? What made it tick? How, under any possible investigative procedure, could a revolutionary with such a conscience be spotted?

To illustrate further the difficulty of detecting the most dangerous traitors and spies, let us look at the case of Bruno Pontecorvo, onetime physicist in the Canadian project in Toronto during the war, and from 1949 until recently one of the top theoretical physicists at the Harwell Laboratory in England.

It may be recalled that Pontecorvo, on a sudden flight from Rome to Helsinki, via Stockholm, disappeared with his wife and two children, probably behind the Iron Curtain. He was presumably motivated by a desire to assist the Russian atomic energy project.

Bruno Pontecorvo was an entirely different type of personality from Fuchs, but one that would perhaps be even more difficult to detect in any investigative procedure. He was a man with a complete absence of fanaticism and moral gloom. Unlike the mousy, retiring Fuchs, Pontecorvo was an extrovert. He was carefree, gregarious, handsome, and athletic. And at the same time he was an able, respected, and imaginative scientist. A thorough investigation of Pontecorvo's background would have revealed something that he never particularly tried to hide, namely, that his brother in Italy was a Communist. And yet, from his demeanor and from anything he ever said or wrote, one would suspect Bruno Pontecorvo least of all the scientists gathered at Harwell.

Different as they may be in personality, both Fuchs and Pontecorvo fall into a category of undesirables which are the most difficult to detect. Such people are drawn by an ideology to find that spot from which they can most effectively commit a traitorous act. They are smart; they are blessed with education; they are self-controlled. No party cards for them, no foolish acts, and no rules and regulations other than the rules and regulations and loyalties of their own creed. And yet they will appear superficially to abide by all the rules and regulations of the society in which they live; there is no evidence of the revolutionary in their day-to-day acts.

These are the people, of course, who can do us the most harm. They are also the people whom we are least likely to suspect. Being smart, composed, and plausible, they will quietly seek their place and bide their time.

Most of the other categories of dangerous people are easier to guard against—for example, the mentally deranged, the overt fanatic, the assassin. These can either be detected by a clever diagnostician, or guarded against by the erection of steel fences and the employment of guards who know how to frustrate their unreasoning plots. These are the "blunt" fanatics, and their very bluntness gives them away.

Also easier to spot are the vocal ideological types who for one reason or another are detractors of our democratic institutions but who, unlike the fanatic, simply want an outlet, an opportunity to speak, and most of all an audience. For these people the Hyde Park treatment and a soapbox audience usually suffice. It is in this group that we find many of the association cases—the joiners of front organizations—and the question is always: "Is he simply a joiner or a well-motivated reformer, or is he, on the other hand, something more dangerous, a potential Fuchs?" Although it is often hard to determine the real motives of these people, it is not hard to discover them.

The mechanics for locating an undesirable are essentially these:

Before anyone may secure a clearance from the Commission for access to classified atomic information he must first fill out a Personnel Security Questionnaire, a "PSQ." This is a form which contains some score or more questions, covering such topics as membership in Communist organizations. A lie here could mean a perjury prosecution. One therefore hesitates to lie.

Next comes the background investigation by the FBI. This includes a check of the individual's file, if any, in FBI headquarters and other law-enforcement agencies, together with an intensive investigation by FBI field agents into all of the past associations of the individual, including interviews with people who have known him. Under a recent change in the law, a substantial number of these investigations will be conducted by a new investigatory office set up in the Civil Service Commission, but the FBI will continue to do a large share of the work, particularly where a question arises, or where the individual being investigated will have access to particularly sensitive information.

Any derogatory information turned up by the background investigation is evaluated by the security officers of the Commission's field offices, and their recommendation is forwarded to the appropriate AEC field office manager. If the manager decides that clearance should be denied, the individual concerned has the right to request a review of his case by a local Personnel Security Review Board composed of persons of the manager's choosing. The individual may appear before the Board, may submit evidence to it, and may be represented by counsel if he wishes. The local AEC manager then makes a new determination based on the recommendation of this Board. If again the clearance is denied, the individual may appeal for another review by the Commission's main Personnel Security Review Board, which is responsible directly to the Commission's General Manager and is composed of leading experts from outside the program. After this review the Commission's General Manager makes a determination which is final.

In all of its considerations having to do with personnel security cases, the Commission follows this general principle:

"The decision as to security clearance is an over-all common-sense judgment, made after consideration of all the relevant information as to whether or not there is risk that the granting of security clearance would endanger the common defense and security. If it is determined that the common defense and security will not be endangered, security clearance will be granted; otherwise, security clearance will be denied." *

* "Criteria for Determining Eligibility for Personnel Security Clearance," Appendix 8, page 188, Fifth Semi-Annual Report of the Atomic Energy Commission to Congress of January 1949.

hurst in Cheshire; and the uranium ore processing center is at Springfields in Lancashire. Harwell, in addition to its research work, provides technological assistance to the production programs, including help in the design of the large plutonium-producing reactors at Sellafield. Britain also has a weapons program under the very capable direction of Dr. W. G. Penny, and tested its first atomic bomb last October in the Monte Bello Islands off the coast of Australia.

The British atomic energy project is therefore a comprehensive and completely integrated one. The British have access to the uranium ore they need; they produce the fissionable materials uranium-235 and plutonium, and they can, and do, make atomic weapons. Their basic and applied research is extensive, and they are exploring diligently the peaceful applications of the atom.

As in the United States, the entire British atomic energy program is under government ownership and control. This was provided for in the British atomic energy act of 1946, which placed the entire program under the Minister of Supply, a member of the Cabinet. He has the power to make grants of public funds for research and production, to build and operate plants and laboratories, and to authorize searches for uranium. He may seize minerals and deposits, and he may prohibit the treatment, processing, or transfer of fissionable materials.

There are many in Britain today who feel that the British program would be much more effective if it were to be established under an independent agency, such as a government corporation, or a commission, as in the United States, rather than as a part of one of the established older departments of government. It is not unlikely, therefore, that in the near future the organizational structure of the British program may be radically changed. But no matter how it is administered, it is quite safe to predict that its output will be impressive and of very high quality. This fact raises the question of what our relations should be with the United Kingdom in the exchange of information in the field of atomic energy.

The partnership of wartime days between the United States and the United Kingdom in the atomic energy field was ended by the prohibitions in the American Atomic Energy Act of 1946, which forbade interchanges of information with foreign countries relating to the production of fissionable materials and the making of atomic weapons. In fact, by one interpretation at least, there can be no exchange of information in the field of atomic power development and production.

There are certain non-sensitive and rather narrow fields, such as health and safety, isotope techniques, and low-power research reactors, where exchanges of information between the two countries and Canada still take place. There is also a close relationship, and there always has been, in the field of uranium ore procurement. Most of the agreements that were entered into several years ago with the countries that produce ore for the Western World were worked out jointly by the United States and the United Kingdom. In addition, there is an agreement between the United States, the United Kingdom, and Canada that no sensitive information jointly shared by the three countries during the war may be declassified or passed on to any other foreign country without the consent of all parties to the agreement. This means that there must be joint conferences from time to time to determine precisely what should be held and what should be released in the way of information. But in every other sense, the wartime co-operation between Britain and the United States has ended.

Few people who have thought about the problem at all believe that it makes very much sense for these two great and traditionally friendly countries to go their separate ways in the new and challenging field of atomic energy. At the same time, however, many of these people feel that until British security methods are tightened, at least to the point where a Bruno Pontecorvo cannot merrily wing his way from Harwell to Russia without some kind of restriction, we cannot afford to be full partners.

In the event of a wholesale aggression against the West by the U.S.S.R., American atomic bombs undoubtedly would be committed to the defense of Britain. It does seem a bit ludicrous, therefore, that the first British bomb should have been detonated without American scientists having had at least a peek at it. If there are novel and useful things about that first British weapon (and the British designers are of the very best), why should they not be incorporated into the bombs that may someday be used to protect England from aggression? And if we can learn something from the British engineers and scientists who are attempting to extract useful power from the atom—as it seems clear we could—shouldn't we be learning?

The goal over the next few years, it would seem to me, should be this: a wide base of co-operation between the scientists and engineers of the United States and Great Britain in the new and challenging field of atomic energy; a co-operation, however, that would be conducted in such a way that the Soviet program would not be advanced.

## CANADA

Canada, unlike the United Kingdom, is not interested in making atomic bombs. She could make them, but she has wisely decided not to expend her energy in this frightfully costly pursuit. She is understandably interested, however, in exploiting in every possible way her abundant uranium resources so that they may contribute to the defense of the Western World and ultimately provide Canada with whatever blessings a split atom may bestow.

Canada first became officially interested in atomic energy in 1940, when the National Research Council began to sponsor nuclear experiments. Late in 1942 Great Britain joined Canada in the establishment of a laboratory at the University of Montreal. Canada provided part of the staff, and Britain sent over a research team, including some French refugee scientists, that had been working at Cambridge University. The Montreal project—later joined by an American team—was interested principally in slow-neutron research, and it maintained close contact with the Americans under Fermi in Chicago who were developing the first chain-reacting pile.

It was early in 1944 that Canada decided to build its first experimental nuclear reactor. The site chosen was Chalk River, 125 miles west of Ottawa. The reactor, utilizing uranium and heavy water, was completed in the fall of 1945—the first reactor to go into operation outside the United States. Called ZEEP (for Zero Energy Experimental Pile), it has no cooling system and can put out but a few watts of energy. The reactor is still in operation, however, and is used primarily as a research instrument in nuclear physics and for testing reactor materials.

In 1947 the Canadians completed a much larger and more powerful reactor, known as NRX (for National Research Experimental), which is also located at Chalk River and which also uses uranium metal with heavy water as the moderator. While NRX is designed in such a way that it can produce only small quantities of plutonium, it for a long time had a greater concentration of neutrons than any other research reactor in the world. This made it uniquely valuable for many types of research and for the production of highly irradiated isotopes. The designed heat output of the NRX reactor is 10,000 kilowatts, but it has normally been operated at higher levels. Late in 1952 an accident occurred in NRX that has temporarily put it out of commission. It is now being re-

The French program, unlike those of the United States, Great Britain, and Canada, has from the very beginning been operated completely in the open. Secrecy is virtually unknown.

The principal installations of the French project are at three locations in the general vicinity of Paris. One is Fort de Chatillon, a short distance southwest of Paris. Here is located the first nuclear reactor to be built in Western Europe, excluding the British Isles. The reactor, called ZOE, has been in operation since December 1948. It is a low-power research reactor using uranium oxide as fuel and heavy water as the moderator.

The second site of French atomic energy activity is Christ de Saclay, seventeen kilometers beyond Chatillon. Saclay is the home of France's second reactor, which began operating last October. Known as P-2, it also uses heavy water as a moderator. Of substantially higher power than ZOE, P-2 can produce significant quantities of plutonium if desired, but the French have announced their intention of using it primarily for isotope production and research purposes. The Saclay laboratory is also a general atomic research center, with equipment including a 25-million-electron-volt accelerator.

France's third atomic energy installation is at Le Bouchet, thirty-five kilometers due south of Paris. Le Bouchet is devoted to uranium chemistry and the preparation of fuel slugs from French uranium deposits for ZOE and P-2.

The French atomic energy program is currently headed by Francis Perrin, a scientist of world-wide reputation who taught physics at Columbia University in 1940 as a visiting professor. The program has over a thousand employees, of whom about a fourth are well-qualified engineers and scientists.

France also has several high-energy accelerators at such locations as the College de France in Paris and the University of Strasbourg, and is installing several more.

She has maintained friendly relations with the scientists of the other countries of Western Europe and is indebted to Norway for the heavy water used in her first reactor. In the Saclay and Chatillon piles she produces radioisotopes in substantial quantities for shipment to hospitals and industrial concerns in France and to neighboring countries. She is also an active member of the ten-country European Research Center established recently just over the French border in Switzerland.

France, therefore, has the talent and the equipment for a fully integrated and well-rounded atomic energy project. Moreover, she has sufficient uranium ore available within her own borders to support an active research and development program, as well as possibly sizable additional reserves in her African colonies. The French know how to process uranium ore and to make it into reactor fuel. And they know how to build reactors that can produce substantial quantities of plutonium that, if the French wished, could be made into atomic weapons.

France at the moment, however, has no weapons program and apparently does not intend in the immediate future to engage in one. Just recently she announced a fifteen-year effort directed toward the development and construction of a network of atomic power plants. For the first five years the French National Assembly has provided $108,000,000 for this program, compared with the $43,-000,000 that was available from 1946 to 1951. France has a strong incentive to develop nuclear power because of her lack of petroleum and the inadequacy of her domestic coal deposits. During the first five years of her fifteen-year power development plan, France expects to build two additional reactors primarily for the production of plutonium fuel at sites yet to be selected.

During the next five years, as plutonium becomes increasingly available in France, there will doubtless be pressures from the French military establishment to get into the weapons business. But France would do well to follow the example of Canada and devote her energies to research and to the realization of the peaceful uses of atomic energy, making her military contribution to the security of the Western World in another area.

## NORWAY *and* THE NETHERLANDS

It is appropriate to discuss the atomic energy programs of these two countries together, for they jointly operate the only nuclear reactor in the free world outside of the United States, Great Britain, Canada, and France. The reactor, located at Kjeller, near Oslo, in Norway, is a research and radioisotope-producing device designed to operate at one hundred kilowatts, although it has been operated at levels as high as three hundred kilowatts. It is called JEEP, and was completed in 1951, utilizing heavy water from Norway and uranium that the foresighted Dutch had purchased in 1939 from Belgium for possible atomic energy use. The uranium was hidden in the Netherlands throughout the German occupation.

The Norwegian-Dutch partnership in atomic energy dates back to 1950, and the Kjeller activity, which includes "hot" laboratories and physics research facilities as well as the reactor, bears the name "Joint Establishment for Nuclear Energy Research." The Establishment is directed by a six-man Atomic Energy Board upon which Norway and the Netherlands have equal representation, and the chairmanship is rotated among all six members. None of the work at Kjeller is secret, and the staff includes people from such other countries as Sweden, Switzerland, Italy, Yugoslavia, and the United States as well as Norway and Holland.

Norway's current interest in atomic energy is not surprising, for the Norsk Hydro Plant at Rjukan has been producing heavy water for use in the nuclear research laboratories of the world since 1934. One of the most colorful chapters of World War II revolves around the efforts of the Germans to obtain heavy water from this plant for their atomic energy program, and the equally determined efforts of the British Commandos and Norwegian underground to keep them from succeeding. Leif Tronstad, professor of chemistry at the Norwegian Institute of Technology in Trondheim and the man who got Norsk Hydro into the heavy-water business in the first place, was killed during the war on a secret mission to Rjukan to prevent German exploitation of the heavy-water plant. The plant was partly destroyed during the war, but it was running full-scale again by 1946, and it provided the heavy water for the Kjeller pile.

In addition to the Kjeller laboratory, Norway also has active nuclear research programs, including the use of Van de Graaff generators and betatrons, at the universities and technical centers in Oslo, Bergen, and Trondheim. Two of Norway's scientists with world-wide reputations in atomic energy are Gunnar Randers, who escaped to England and America during the war and is presently director of the Kjeller project; and Odd Dahl, who supervised construction of the Kjeller reactor. Dahl is a leading figure in the new European Research Laboratory in Switzerland.

Norway's principal immediate reasons for supporting an atomic energy program appear to be, first, her desire to rehabilitate her war-ravaged scientific strength and thus keep her young scientists at home, and, second, to produce radioisotopes, for which there is a large demand in Norwegian industrial, research, and medical centers. For the long term Norway, even though she is one of the world's best-endowed nations from the standpoint of falling water, is nevertheless also interested in the development of atomic power. With one of the world's principal merchant marines, she is particularly interested in the

Research Center. Italy has the talent and equipment to build a research reactor, and it would not be surprising if she undertook such a project within the next few years. She does not appear to have the resources at present, however, for a large-scale program. As to uranium, some low-grade deposits have been reported at various places in Italy, but they are not being extensively worked.

## SWITZERLAND

The Swiss have had a Research Commission for Atomic Energy since late 1945, and the government supports work at the Federal Institute of Technology in Zurich, where there is a thirty-eight-inch cyclotron, as well as at the universities of Zurich, Basel, Berne, Geneva, Lausanne, and Neuchâtel. Switzerland regularly imports radioisotopes for use in hospitals and research laboratories, and her distinguished medical community has made useful contributions in the application of isotopes in diagnosis and therapy.

Switzerland has long had a special interest in the development of atomic energy to produce useful power. Her efforts along these lines, however, have been severely handicapped by her lack of uranium. The Swiss nevertheless look forward to the day when they can build their first nuclear reactor.

It seems quite reasonable to expect that nuclear research in Switzerland will receive a substantial shot in the arm as operation of the Central European Research Laboratory near Geneva gets under way. The first equipment to be installed there will be the largest and most powerful particle accelerator in the world, and Swiss scientists, under the direction of Paul Scherrer of the Federal Institute of Technology, are expected to play an important part in the work of the laboratory.

INDIA

Among the nations of Asia, India has the largest and most advanced atomic energy program. It is a peaceful program, directed toward exploiting the atom as a source of power, and it is carried out under the control and supervision of the Indian Atomic Energy Commission, which was set up in 1948 when the Indian Atomic Energy Act was adopted. The Indian AEC, which sponsors research projects in a number of educational and scientific institutions throughout the country, is a three-man body reporting direct to the prime minister.

The leading nuclear research center in India is the Tata Institute of Fundamental Research at Bombay, which is currently looking into the possibilities of producing heavy water and of building a nuclear reactor. The Institute of Nuclear Physics in Calcutta is also being built up to a leading position, and recently added a thirty-two-inch cyclotron, the only such machine in India. Atomic energy research is also in progress at the Bose Research Institute in Calcutta, the University of Delhi, the Indian Institute of Science at Bangalore, the Physical Research Laboratory at Ahmedabad, and Aligarh University, among other places.

India has made a good deal of progress in recent years in cosmic-ray research, and in the training of her physicists, chemists, and engineers for specialized work in atomic energy. Among her accomplishments, also, is the development of a program for the use of radioisotopes in medicine, including the diagnosis and treatment of certain types of cancer and leukemia. In an effort to build up her contacts with the world scientific community, India has stimulated visits by foreign scientists and encouraged their residence there for periods as long as a year or more.

India has some uranium; enough, she hopes, to make her independent of outside sources of supply. She has been very active in the search for atomic energy minerals, and has a standing offer, as we do in the United States, to buy at a guaranteed price all stocks of uranium discovered. She also offers rewards for the discovery of new deposits, and grants allowances for the development of mines. Of possible great future significance is the fact that India has probably the world's richest deposits of monazite, a sand containing thorium. Thorium, potentially, can be used like uranium as a source of atomic energy. A factory to treat fifteen hundred tons of monazite sand a year is in operation in southwest India.

Under the leadership of some very able scientists, India has made a determined effort to keep posted on nuclear research developments the world over, and, although she currently has only limited funds and trained personnel, she should score some real gains in the relatively near future. Right now she is looking forward to the construction of her first reactor, for research and radioisotope production, within the next two years.

BRAZIL

Brazil, in atomic energy, is to South America what India is to Asia; namely, the most aggressive country on the continent. Her program of atomic energy research and development is under the control and direction of the National Research Council, which was established in 1951. The president and vice-president of the Council are officers of the armed forces, and the members include many other government officials and scientists.

Brazil's nuclear research work centers around the Brazilian Center of Physical Research in Rio and the University of São Paulo, although there are a half-dozen or so additional institutions where noteworthy projects are under way, including the University of Brazil in Rio. The most ambitious project yet undertaken in Brazil will be the construction of a 450-million-electron-volt synchrocyclotron at the Center of Physical Research. A small cyclotron for the Center is now being built at the University of Chicago, and American scientists are assisting the Brazilians in developing plans for the larger machine. The University of São Paulo already has a thirty-million-volt betatron and a Van de Graaff generator.

Brazil has some very competent young scientists, including C. M. G. Lattes (presently head of Center of Physical Research), who in 1947 participated in the discovery of the subatomic particle, the meson, while studying cosmic rays. A year later, while at the University of California in Berkeley, he also participated in the discovery of the artificial production of mesons in the 184-inch cyclotron there. Many people consider the discovery and subsequent study of the meson to be the most important development in nuclear physics since the end of the war. Brazil is also well known to the American atomic energy program as the largest importer of radioisotopes in Latin America, and as a nation which actively encourages exchange visits between her scientists and those of the United States and other countries.

All of Brazil's current atomic energy effort is regarded by the National Research Council as preliminary to achievement of the main goal: construction of a real nuclear reactor for research, training, and isotope-production purposes, leading to eventual utilization of the atom to produce power for commerce and industry.

Among Brazil's natural resources of potential value to an atomic energy program are some sizable deposits of monazite, source of thorium. These are not so large, however, as those of India. While some prospecting has been undertaken for uranium at various locations over Brazil's vast land area, an intensive exploration program has never really been attempted. This is unfortunate. If and when Brazil locates large deposits of uranium ore, as she well may, we may expect a real intensification of her atomic energy effort. Such an exploration effort, it would seem,

sources that are essential to a large industrial operation such as an atomic energy program.

As nearly everyone knows, the Russians in their efforts to make industrial progress have been employing a series of so-called "five-year plans." There are approximately two years remaining in the current one, and, even if they do not reach their goals, which are pretentious, they will nevertheless have the makings of an ominous war machine geared to the manufacture and use of either conventional or atomic weapons. I think it is worth mentioning that we in the United States, under our democratic form of government, cannot enjoy the "luxury" of five-year plans. Here we operate under a series of "one-year plans" called fiscal years. At the beginning of each fiscal year our Atomic Energy Commission and our Defense Department must go to the Congress and lay out their plans for the coming twelve months and request the money needed to accomplish them. Very occasionally, on specific items where long-term contracts must be entered into, they can obtain an authorization to spend money over longer periods, but over-all production plans can be made with certitude only for the duration of the fiscal year. There is no doubt that this puts us at a distinct disadvantage in our competition with the vastly more integrated and long-range production programs of the totalitarian Communist states.

The growth in Russian output of coal, steel, aluminum, electric power, and petroleum will be truly enormous under the current five-year plan. Here are just a few examples:

By 1955 the U.S.S.R. will surpass the 1952 United States coal-production figure. She will increase aluminum production to 50 per cent of the 1952 figure for the United States (and as late as 1930 no aluminum was produced in the Soviet Union). Electric generating capacity will also climb to around half that of the United States. And steel production will increase 62 per cent over the current five-year plan to a tonnage figure equal to about 50 per cent of the United States output. Weak only in petroleum and rail transport, Russia is pushing vigorously ahead in both of these areas.

Although these and other figures like them show that the Soviet Union is still running somewhat behind the United States in the production of industrial materials, they also show an almost explosive rate of increase in the production of raw materials—a trend that, if continued, will bring her up to American production levels in a very short period of time. It should also be remembered, when considering these relative figures, that in Russia far less of the production of these essential materials is diverted into such things as automobiles, race tracks, hotels, and electrical appliances. It goes, instead, for increasing the productive capacity still further, and for articles of war.

### Scientific Capability:

Some of the best advice that has been given on what the American attitude toward Russian science should be came from Lazar Volin, of the U. S. Department of Agriculture, at a symposium held in December 1951 at a meeting of the American Association for the Advancement of Science in Philadelphia. This is what he said:

"It is a fact that many branches of science in Russia during the early years of the present century were already marching steadily ahead in full step with scientific advances elsewhere. This is fairly well known in scientific circles, where it is appreciated that a very substantial legacy of science, as of culture generally, was inherited by the Soviet regime. But it is not so well realized, I am afraid, by the layman in the West. He has been misled and confused by the Soviet propagandists and their mouthpieces, who, after long harping on the extreme cultural backwardness of Russia prior to the Revolution, have more recently made profuse claims of Russia's priority in many scientific

Kapitza, Fellow of the Royal Society of Great Britain, Director of the Royal Society's Mond Laboratory at Cambridge University, and one of the world's foremost experts on low-temperature studies. Kapitza had received his training in physics at the Petrograd Institute of Technology, completing his work about the time of the 1917 Revolution. He remained at this Institute (renamed Leningrad Tech) as a lecturer until 1921, when he left Russia for Cambridge, England. At Cambridge he rose rapidly until he became director of the Mond Laboratory and won a respected place for himself in world science.

Each year while he was in England Kapitza returned to Russia for a short visit. In advance of each of these visits he obtained a letter from Russian authorities assuring that a return visa would be issued to him. In 1935, however, he was persuaded not to request such a letter, on the grounds that it made him appear not to trust the Soviet government. He did not request the letter; he went to Russia for his annual visit, and he never came out. Although it is not known exactly what was said to Kapitza when he returned to Russia in 1935, it might well have gone something like this:

"Peter Leonidovich, we are proud of you and what you have done for Russian science in the West. We don't blame you for leaving in 1921, but now we would like to have you back. Things have changed a lot since you left. Those coarse fellows who made everything so difficult back in the early 1920's are no longer in a position of authority, and, under our great leader Stalin, the inherent value of science and scientists to Soviet society and culture is well recognized. If you remain you will have your own laboratory with all the equipment and staff you need; you will be paid well; and you will have an honored place in the society of our country. We want you to stay, and besides that, it will be impossible for you to leave even if you want to."

But whatever was said, and whatever motivated Kapitza, he remained in Russia. Until about four years ago he applied his brilliant talent and valuable experience to the objectives of Soviet science as Director of the Institute for Physical Problems of the Academy of Sciences of the U.S.S.R. in Moscow. The honors he received include two Stalin prizes, in 1941 and 1943, and the Order of Lenin in 1943.

For the past four years, however, he has been under what amounts essentially to house arrest in his home outside Moscow, apparently for failure to continue to follow government instructions. His only public appearances are occasional lectures in Moscow.

Another result of the Soviet government's increased interest in science in the 1930's was the almost inevitable injection of the "party line" into certain areas of scientific inquiry, particularly those where some Marxist principle was at stake. At the American Association for the Advancement of Science's symposium on Soviet science in 1951, published by the National Science Foundation in the book *Soviet Science*, most of the expert American observers of the Russian scientific scene who participated in the discussions agreed that unscientific political influences had penetrated many Soviet fields of scientific endeavor and badly damaged some. The field most affected is probably genetics, where the quackery of the now notorious Lysenko dominates Soviet thinking with the full backing of the Soviet government. Other fields in which governmental interference has hurt science and lifted quacks to positions of great prestige and influence are psychology, psychiatry, physiology, pathology, and biology. The fields most free of this kind of interference are physics, chemistry, and mathematics, and these, significantly, are the lines of scientific endeavor that are most vital to a sturdy atomic energy program. Although ideology is a factor in the esteem with which notable foreign physicists, chemists, and mathematicians are regarded in Russia, this usually does not interfere with the utilization of their discoveries in Russian physics, chemistry, and mathematics. Einstein, for example, is looked upon as being rather too much of an idealist to be rated highly as an individual in Communist eyes, but this does not prevent the Russians from accepting his theory that matter can be transformed into energy, as in an A-bomb explosion.

To obtain some feeling for the quality of Russian physics, chemistry, and mathematics today, there are several places the average American layman can look. There are, for example, the judgments of the American experts who know Russia best. Of these, a good example is John Turkevich of the Department of Chemistry at Princeton University, who, with his wife Ludmilla, is employed by the Atomic Energy Commission's Brookhaven National Laboratory to translate Russian scientific papers for the benefit of American researchers. This is what Turkevich says about Russian physics and chemistry: "It is evident to any observer that Soviet chemistry and physics is a well organized body of well trained scientists carrying out creditable work in many branches of their subject in the best tradition of the West."

Another such expert is J. R. Kline of the Mathematics Department of the University of Pennsylvania, a leading student of Russian mathematical activity. This is what he says: "I would like to describe Soviet mathematics as a most active and fruitful activity where fundamental results are being obtained and where there is no evidence of thought control." Russia has always been very strong in mathematics, and American mathematical science received a real assist from a group of Russian mathematicians who left the Soviet Union about the time of the Revolution to take teaching positions at such American institutions as Stanford, Dartmouth, Brown, and the universities of Michigan and Pennsylvania.

Then consider the known accomplishments of Russian scientists in non-secret areas. The following random facts are both interesting and revealing:

1. In 1927 the Russian physicist Skobelzyn substantially advanced nuclear research by adapting the Wilson cloud chamber to the study of cosmic rays.

2. The first cyclotron in Europe was built at the Radium Institute in Moscow in 1937.

3. In 1939 the two Russian physicists Flerov and Petrazhak announced their discovery of the spontaneous fission of uranium.

4. In 1945 the Russian physicist Veksler developed and put forward the idea of the synchrotron about the same time that it was proposed independently by the American scientist McMillan of the Radiation Laboratory of the University of California. A synchrotron is generally similar to a cyclotron, but is of advanced design.

Still another good indication of the competence of Russian scientists is the information that is published in Russian scientific journals, of which there are many. Scientific publications are always a good clue to the scientific health and activity of a nation, even though today, especially in Russia, a good deal of what is accomplished is never published where it would be exposed to prying Western eyes. But enough is still published to tell us that scientific activity in Russia today is very vigorous.

Until 1947 all scientific papers published in Russia bore titles and abstracts in English or German as well as in Russian, and two periodicals, the *Journal of Physics* and *Acta Physicochimica*, were published in all three languages. In 1947, however, this practice was discontinued, and today Russian scientific publications are printed only in Russian, thus making it even more difficult for Western scientists to keep contact with the work of their Russian colleagues. It is to help overcome this latest obstacle that the U. S. Atomic Energy Commission's Brookhaven National Labo-

big things to be done in a big way—at a price in human freedom and dignity. Among her at least superficial advantages is her almost unlimited supply of slave and prison labor, which, in Russian eyes, need not be fed, clothed, or treated decently and humanely. With plenty of labor and with the concept that this labor is expendable, she automatically eliminates the elaborate and costly health and safety devices which a democracy must employ—and should employ.

Among the disadvantages of her system is the fact that scientists and engineers do not work honestly and boldly —and therefore at their best—under the eyes of the secret police. This is not the kind of atmosphere in which ideas are nurtured and brave new things are tried. It is the kind of atmosphere that produces fear, and with fear comes caution and conservatism. There are many examples of this.

In 1942 a Russian delegation came to this country to secure information on various petroleum-refining methods. After considerable study the delegation chose a method known as the "Houdry process" as the one they wanted under Lend-Lease. At that time the Houdry process was the only catalytic cracking process that had several years of proved refinery operation behind it. Other methods had been developed, but they had not been completely perfected. Some of these, however, gave evidence of soon outstripping the Houdry process in economy and production, and had, in fact, been almost universally accepted in 1942 for all future catalytic cracking units that were subsequently installed in the U.S. Although information on the other processes was made available to the Russians, along with the Houdry method, they were unwilling to gamble on what, from an engineering point of view, was a relatively sure thing.

Russian science has also suffered over the years from purges. This should be a lesson to us. Whenever the government attempted to bend scientific findings to make them fit some political pronouncement of Marx or Lenin or Stalin, science suffered, and one finds such scientific quacks as Lysenko in positions of great influence in Russian science. To date, these scientific frauds have not penetrated into an activity so vital to Soviet aggrandizement as atomic energy, but under the totalitarian Communist system, such a possibility always exists.

The Russian program teaches us another lesson: One always pays a heavy price for compartmentalization as an aid to security. To be sure, it is safer to hold certain information to a limited few; but this frequently reduces the rate of progress. We have found in the American program, for example, that when we call in all of our laboratories—not just one—to tackle a problem, our rate of progress frequently increases almost by as many times as the number of laboratories called in. The Russians, under their system of compartmentalization, attempt to achieve the development of new ideas at no risk to security by the device of assigning one—and only one—of their institutes a high-priority task calling for all of the talents available in that institute. I suggest, however, that on some occasions they have thereby achieved a high degree of security at a cost that must be measured in terms of a heavy loss in ideas.

But on the "advantage" side, the reader should bear in mind that Russia can compel any priorities that she desires, and that a vast spy network, which has been obviously successful in the past, serves her military atomic energy program. He should also have in mind that Comrade Beria, who so recently headed the atomic effort, was also in charge of slave labor and the secret police. These three activities are closely related in the Russian atomic energy program. It might also be well if they had a relationship in the minds of the peoples of the free world, for, if Russia's atomic energy program is sufficiently successful to

In addition, the next ten years should see the use of atomic engines, not only in submarines, but also in large surface vessels, such as aircraft carriers of the U. S. Navy —*if* we want them. It is also possible, although less likely, that an atomic propulsion plant will be developed that could be used economically in commercial ships. We may not see all this in ten years, but it is virtually certain that we could see it within the next fifteen—again, *if* we want to.

Another possibility for the next decade is an atomic-powered aircraft for the Air Force. Whether this is achieved depends almost solely on how much money the government is willing to spend annually on its development. I would doubt, however—no matter how much money is spent—that there will be any atomic-powered airplanes in commercial use within ten years, although it is quite possible that this will become a reality later on.

One place where the atomic engine may come into its own is in the now all but forgotten field of dirigibles. A dirigible could carry aloft the very heavy shielding required for an atomic engine much more easily than could an airplane. The danger of fire would also be greatly reduced by the use of atomic fuels, for they will not burn in the sense that gasoline or oil will. Although I would be a little surprised if any atomic-powered dirigibles were to be in commercial service by 1963, I believe an experimental model could be in the air by that time if someone were willing to pay for it. I can see no reason why someday, possibly within fifteen or twenty years, such aircraft should not be available for commercial use.

I believe it would even be possible within the next decade to have atomic-powered locomotives. I should be surprised, however, if this were attempted by so early a date. The special hazards presented by an atomic engine and the expense of developing one that might fit a locomotive efficiently suggest that other possible uses of atomic power will be developed first.

In regard to atomic-powered automobiles, which have been discussed a good deal, I feel that they are out of the question, not only for the next decade, but probably forever. The very heavy and bulky shielding required to seal in the deadly radiations emanating from atomic reactions would seem to preclude their use in so small a vehicle. Also, an atomic reaction requires a minimum amount of nuclear fuel (a "critical mass") before it will operate. The amount of power needed to propel an automobile is far less than the amount that can be produced by a critical mass of nuclear fuel. This would therefore seem to be a highly inefficient use of so valuable a source of power. There is, however, a chance that someone may someday find a way to convert the very intense radioactivity of the ashes of a nuclear fire (fission products) into heat. If this were accomplished it might be possible to use small quantities of these ashes to produce heat to drive such small vehicles as automobiles. I cannot see this being done within the next decade, however.

Another suggested use of atomic fuel about which there has been a good deal of speculation is the propulsion of interplanetary rockets or space ships. There is one major drawback here. An aircraft or guided missile using an atomic reactor for power could propel itself through the earth's atmosphere by taking air in through the front of the craft, heating and thereby expanding it, and then ejecting it out the rear, in the manner of a jet. But in space there is no atmosphere. An atomic space ship would therefore have to carry along some substance which could be heated and ejected in order to propel itself. The problems of weight and bulk that face the designers of space craft are therefore not automatically solved by atomic energy.

In general, in the field of power I look for atomic energy to be utilized gradually where large sources of power are required, such as in central-station electric generating plants, in ships, and possibly in some types of large aircraft. I do not look for it to be used, at least for some time, where very small sources of power are needed, such as in house furnaces, small aircraft, or, as we have seen, in automobiles. But the use of atomic energy where large sources of power are required will certainly free our supplies of oil, coal, and gas for wider use in other places.

In fields other than power, I would expect that during the next decade radioisotopes and other sources of nuclear radiation will come into ever wider use in medicine, industry, and agriculture. More people will be trained in the techniques of using them, and the lives of more people will be helpfully affected by them. But the chances of something really spectacular occurring in this field in the next decade are little better than even. The most likely possibilities are in cancer research, where some important advances will very likely be made (although a single complete "cure" for all and any types of cancer is unlikely); in the study of photosynthesis, where there is a chance that man may uncover the secret of what makes plants grow; and in the utilization of highly radioactive materials for such purposes as the production of new chemicals or the sterilization of drugs and possibly some foods.

"But what," you may well ask, "will all this mean to me?" If you live in the industrialized East, it may mean that within ten years you will be using in your home electricity that is produced in an atomic power plant. As I have stated earlier in this book, this probably will not change your electric-light bill very much, but it may very well make your city a cleaner and more attractive place in which to live, for no smoke or fumes emerge from such a plant. Your chances of having a small reactor in your basement to provide heat and electricity directly for your home, however, are virtually nil for the next ten years and probably for many decades after that, if not forever.

If you live in an undeveloped part of the country, such as sections of the Rocky Mountain region, your chances of being more directly affected by the coming of atomic power are somewhat greater. It may be, for example, that you will have large quantities of electricity available where before you had none or very little. It may mean some mineral deposits can be worked that are now undeveloped for lack of power, or that some areas can be irrigated that are now barren because there is no power, or not enough power, to pump in fresh water. The presence of ample power may also mean that new industries will move into your section in order to be closer to the raw materials produced there. I doubt, however, that more than the very beginnings of these changes will be noticeable in ten years.

No matter where you live, there is an excellent chance that within the next decade either your life or the life of someone you know will be saved or prolonged or made more comfortable by the use of radioisotopes. There is also an excellent chance that you will have occasion to buy some industrial product, such as a tire or an engine lubricant or a detergent, that has either been developed or improved through work with radioisotopes. If you are a farmer, there is every likelihood that you will use some information, given you by your county agent or local agricultural experiment station, that has been derived from experimentation with radioisotopes. Work with these immensely valuable materials will affect you increasingly in scores of different ways as time passes.

These, however, are only the things that we know about and can predict with some degree of certainty on the basis of the knowledge we already have. I believe, and I feel that nearly everyone connected with the atomic energy program believes, that there is more in the atom than this. But even if there is not, it is still possible for us to visualize an era in which new opportunities for employment and investment will be created, new regions of the earth opened up and developed, new products produced and marketed, and new life-saving techniques introduced into the world of medicine. The atomic age can be a hopeful, prosperous, and happy age. Or, as has been said many times in the past, it can be the age in which man finally succeeds in destroying himself.

The other side of the atom—the weapons side—is very real. There is no point in trying to pretend that it doesn't exist or that it is not a dangerous threat to civilization. The simple truth is that the weapons stockpiles that are being accumulated in various countries of the world today are rapidly approaching the point where mankind will have the capability to destroy everything on earth. The central problem of the atomic age, obviously, is to avoid such a holocaust. This is not a scientific or technical problem, however; it is a political one, and if it is to be solved it must be solved by diplomatic and political means.

Wars and threats of wars have been a part of man's life all through history. Although many have tried, no one has yet solved the problem of war. But now the atomic age has introduced a new factor that must be taken into the calculations. Whereas before the problem was simply one of war or peace, it is now one of oblivion or peace. With a question like this, it is hard to imagine any answer except peace. Yet man, even in the atomic age, has not chosen peace. He also has not chosen oblivion, and he seems to think he can go on forever without deciding upon one or the other. Maybe he can, but the risks are enormous.

In this situation, there is one thing that clearly suggests itself as a desirable and perhaps necessary step. This is to undertake an intensive educational campaign to show the people of this country, of the Soviet Union, and of the entire world what atomic and hydrogen weapons can really do. As part of this step, I think we must give the public some idea of the magnitude of our stockpile and its tremendous destructive potential. In flirting with world war in the atomic age, man is not playing with fire, he is playing with the means by which mortal life on earth can be ended.

The decision to undertake a real educational campaign of this nature is not something that can be done alone by one agency of government, such as the Atomic Energy Commission. Such a program would have to be undertaken by the whole government, and the whole government, including both the Executive Branch and the Congress, would have to agree that it was a worth-while and necessary thing to do. But if it is undertaken, it will at least provide the peoples of the world, including the diplomats, with an accurate idea of the nature of the choice that faces them. If they have been unable to make the right choice in partial ignorance, perhaps they will be encouraged to make it if they are given a true picture of the tremendously destructive potential of the world's stockpile of atomic weapons.

Continued procrastination by the nations of the world in the area of peace and war need not necessarily be fatal, of course. If no permanent and secure peace is achieved, it is possible for the world to continue to exist in a state of uneasy truce. The risks of such a situation, however, are naturally great. Unless a real and secure peace can be achieved, we have no choice but to remain strong in the hope that the hand of a potential aggressor will be stayed by the threat of absolute retaliation before he makes the irrevocable move. Here again the atom plays a leading role. If world wars cannot be eliminated in the atomic age through agreement, perhaps they can be eliminated through fear of retaliation. This has been the case during the past eight years, and it may be possible to extend this situation indefinitely. Although it is a very weak reed upon which to lean, it is certainly better, in my view, than surrendering our freedom, our dignity, and all we hold dear to Russian Communism, or inviting Soviet aggression through unilateral disarmament.

Our national policy today is to deter aggression while we continue to look for the avenue that might lead to a real peace, and while we build up the economic and defensive strength of our friends and allies in the free world. The atom is vital to all of these goals. It is the bulwark of our plans for the defense of ourselves and our allies; it is the "big stick" that we hope may ultimately encourage the nations of the world to establish a secure peace, and it is an important means by which we may help to improve the economic health of the free world.

The importance of atomic energy to the future economic health of the free world must not be underrated. If the present uneasy truce between the East and the West continues indefinitely, it will probably be because the Soviet Union is betting that the industrial economy of the Western nations will ultimately collapse through overproduction, unemployment, and depression. It is axiomatic that we cannot afford to let this happen. Atomic energy can help to keep it from happening. One of the secrets of the success of Western democracy is that it contains within itself the means by which its economy can be constantly rejuvenated. By providing for free enterprise and the stimulation of competition, the West has produced one new industry after another that has kept its economy from becoming stagnant. Examples are the automobile industry, the aircraft industry, and, more recently, the electronics and synthetic-fibre industries.

Now it is the atomic energy industry. Atomic energy can help the economy of the free world in at least three ways: It can provide a new, inexpensive source of power that can help reduce industrial production costs in many parts of Europe and elsewhere; it can create new markets for the industrial production of Europe and America by helping to open up and develop the backward areas of the world; and, while it is building, it can create new demands for technical equipment and materials that can inject a fresh life into the industrial economy of the West. There is, therefore, a national and international security reason why we should pursue as vigorously as we can the development of the peaceful applications of atomic energy.

If we are to work toward these goals, however, we must have a strong and clearly defined program for the immediate future. My program would consist of the following basic elements:

1. The vigorous prosecution of a never-ceasing effort to bring a real and stable peace to the world.

2. In the absence of a stable peace, no loss of time or momentum in the huge construction program now under way and, above all, no cutback in this program. The facilities now being built should represent the last substantial plant and equipment outlay for the production of fissionable material, but they should be built as fast as possible and operated at full capacity until we have all of the weapons we will need to destroy completely the power of any aggressor to make war.

3. A vigorous basic and applied research program designed to keep in front of the whole world all phases of the field of atomic energy.

4. An atomic energy law flexible enough to permit the Atomic Energy Commission and industry to develop economically feasible power either independently or jointly.

5. A law flexible enough to give the Commission power to trade information on atomic power with countries supplying ore to the United States, as well as, at the appropriate time, with potential suppliers of ore and to countries friendly with the United States who have a special interest in power or other peaceful products of atomic energy.

6. An intensive public-information program to familiar-

# INDEX

AB Atomenergi, 273

Academy of Engineering Science, Stockholm, 273

Academy of Sciences of the U.S.S.R., 289, 294, 297, 298

Acheson, Dean, 25

Acheson-Lilienthal Report, 25, 28

Agriculture Department, 200

aircraft reactor, 157, 221, 311

Alamogordo, N. M., 17

Allis-Chalmers Manufacturing Co., 16

American Association for the Advancement of Science, Symposium on Soviet Science, 294

appropriations, 71 ff., 133

Argentina, 282

Argonne National Laboratory, 67, 150, 155, 176, 180, 219, 223, 225, 239, 271. *See also* Chicago, University of

Army Corps of Engineers, 86

atom smashers (cyclotrons, etc.), 189, 190, 210–14, 224, 225, 296

Atomic Energy Act of 1946, 22, 23, 135, 164, 167, 168, 170, 171, 227, 258, 319

Atomic Energy Commission, 19 ff., 26 ff., 319

Atomic Energy Control Board of Canada, 262

Atomic Energy of Canada, 262

atomic power, 149 ff.; first produced, 153, 154, 159, 163; economic feasibility, 159 ff., 175, 176; policy, 165 ff.; importance,

atomic power (*continued*)
176 ff.; promise, 181–3, 310 ff., 317

Australia, 41, 281

Bacher, Robert L., 28

Bakker, C. J., 253, 269

Barnard, Chester I., 25

Baruch, Bernard, 25

Bechtel Corp., 166

Becquerel, H., 243

Belgian Congo, 30, 32, 38–40, 43, 270

Belgium, 252, 270, 271

Bennett, W. J., 262

Berkeley Radiation Laboratory, 26, 67, 211–14, 225. *See also* California, University of

Bethe, Hans, 218

Bettis Laboratory, Pittsburgh, 67, 221

Bohr, Niels, 218, 243–6, 253, 273, 274

Boothy, Robert, 7

Boulder, Col., 81

Bradbury, Norris, 218, 250

Bradley, Gen. Omar, 136, 137

Brazil, 41, 279–81

Brazilian Center of Nuclear Research, Rio, 279

breeding, 153, 178 ff., 310

British Scientific Mission, 17, 18, 218, 232, 250, 251, 255

Brookhaven National Laboratory, 67, 152, 195, 211, 213, 214, 223, 225, 253, 295

## A NOTE ON THE TYPE

*THE TEXT of this book is set in* Caledonia, *a Linotype face designed by W. A. Dwiggins. It belongs to the family of printing types called "modern face" by printers—a term used to mark the change in style of type-letters that occurred about 1800. Caledonia borders on the general design of Scotch Modern, but is more freely drawn than that letter.*

*The book was composed, printed, and bound by The Plimpton Press, Norwood, Massachusetts. Binding design by W. A. Dwiggins.*